First Edition

Common Core
Support Coach

TARGET ⟩ Foundational Mathematics ③

Dr. Jerry Kaplan
Senior Mathematics Consultant

Common Core Support Coach, Target: Foundational Mathematics, First Edition, Grade 3
T198NA ISBN: 978-1-61997-974-1
Contributing Writers: Q2A/Bill Smith **Cover Design:** Q2A/Bill Smith

Triumph Learning® 136 Madison Avenue, 7th Floor, New York, NY 10016

Contents

Understanding Unit Fractions

PLUG IN · Finding Equal Parts

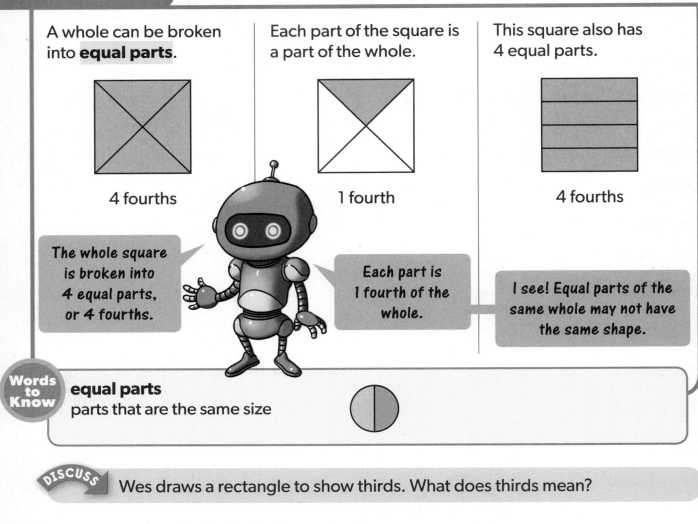

A whole can be broken into **equal parts**.

4 fourths

The whole square is broken into 4 equal parts, or 4 fourths.

Each part of the square is a part of the whole.

1 fourth

Each part is 1 fourth of the whole.

This square also has 4 equal parts.

4 fourths

I see! Equal parts of the same whole may not have the same shape.

Words to Know

equal parts
parts that are the same size

DISCUSS Wes draws a rectangle to show thirds. What does thirds mean?

A You can break a shape into equal parts.

DO Break the shape into thirds.

1 How many parts?

2 Are the parts equal? Write *yes* or *no*.

3 How many thirds?

4 Tell about each part.

___3___ parts

equal: _____

The whole rectangle is equal to _____ thirds.

Each part is _____ third of the whole.

B A shape can be broken into equal parts in more than one way.

> Be careful! Equal parts of the same whole are not always the same.

DO

❶ Count equal parts.

❷ Compare equal parts.

Rectangle *A*   Rectangle *B*

Rectangle A: ___3___ equal parts

Rectangle B: _____ equal parts

Are the equal parts in Rectangle A the same as those in Rectangle B? _____

C You can draw lines to break a shape into equal parts.

DO

❶ Break the circle into halves.

❷ How many equal parts?

❸ Count the halves.

❹ Tell about each part.

___2___ equal parts

The whole circle is equal to _____ halves.

Each part is _____ half of the whole.

PRACTICE

You can show fourths in different ways.

1

Rectangle *A*   Rectangle *B*

Rectangle A: ___4___ equal parts

Rectangle B: _____ equal parts

Are the equal parts in Rectangle *A* the same as those in Rectangle *B*? _____

Draw lines to break the rectangle into fourths. Then write the answers.

2

How many equal parts? _____

The whole rectangle is equal to _____ fourths. Each part is _____ fourth of the whole.

Understanding Fractional Parts of a Number Line

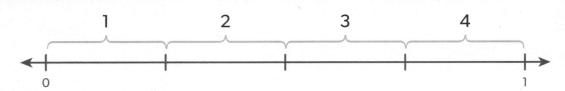

A **number line** can be divided into smaller equal parts of the whole.

Each part of the number line is a part of the whole.

> The number line is divided into 4 equal parts, or fourths.

> Each part is 1 fourth of the whole.

Words to Know

number line
a line with equally placed tic marks named by numbers

DISCUSS   What does it mean to say a number line is divided into fourths?

A A number line between 0 and 1 can be divided into equal parts.

DO

❶ Count the equal parts between 0 and 1 on the number line.

❷ Label each equal part of the number line.

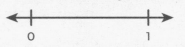

❸ Count the thirds.

❹ Tell about each part.

_____**3**____ equal parts

The whole number line is equal to _____ thirds.

Each part is _____ third of the whole.

B You can divide a number line into equal parts.

A number line can show equal parts of a whole.

DO

❶ Divide the number line into halves.

0   1

❷ How many equal parts?   __2__ equal parts

❸ Count the halves.   The whole number line is equal to _____ halves.

❹ Tell about each part.   Each part is _____ half of the whole.

DISCUSS

Sophia drew this number line. She says each part of the number line represents one fourth. What can you tell Sophia about her work?

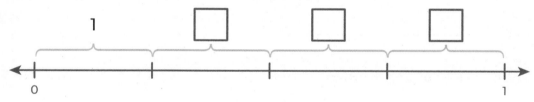
0   1

PRACTICE

Answer the question about the number line.

1

1   ☐   ☐   ☐

0   1

How many equal parts? __4__

The whole number line is _____ fourths.

Each part is _____ fourth of the whole.

Draw marks to separate the number line into thirds. Then write the answers.

2

0   1

How many equal parts? _____

The whole number line is equal to _____ thirds.

Each part is _____ third of the whole.

7

A **unit fraction** names one equal part of a whole.

The **denominator** tells the number of equal parts. It is the bottom number of the fraction.

The **numerator** tells the number of parts you are counting. It is the top number of the fraction.

The dot on the number line shows a fraction.

The number line is separated into 4 equal parts. The denominator is 4.

I see! I counted 1 part of the number line. The numerator is 1. So the fraction is $\frac{1}{4}$.

Words to Know

unit fraction
names one equal part of a whole

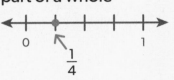

$\frac{1}{4}$

denominator
the total number of equal parts

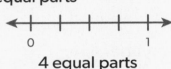

4 equal parts

numerator
the number of parts being counted

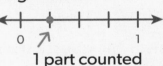

1 part counted

DISCUSS What does the fraction $\frac{1}{2}$ mean?

LESSON LINK

PLUG IN | **POWER UP** | **GO!**

Shapes can be broken into equal parts.

3 equal parts

A number line can be divided into equal parts.

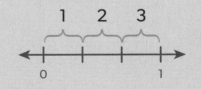

3 thirds

I get it! I can model unit fractions with shapes or number lines.

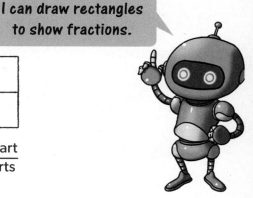

I can draw rectangles to show fractions.

WORK TOGETHER

Use rectangles to show fractions.

- This rectangle shows a fraction.
- There are 4 equal parts. 1 part is shaded.
- So the fraction is $\frac{1}{4}$.

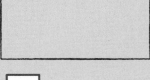

$\frac{1}{4}$ ← shaded part / equal parts

A Model the fraction $\frac{1}{6}$.

DO

① Draw a rectangle.

② Divide the rectangle into 6 equal parts.

③ Shade 1 of the parts.

④ Write the unit fraction.

← shaded part
← equal parts

B Model the fraction $\frac{1}{3}$.

DO

① Draw a rectangle.

② Divide the rectangle into 3 equal parts.

③ Shade 1 of the parts.

④ Write the unit fraction.

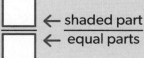

← shaded part
← equal parts

Remember, a fraction names equal parts of a whole.

DISCUSS

William wants to draw a rectangle to model the fraction $\frac{1}{8}$. He says the 8 parts of his rectangle do not need to be the same size. Is William correct? Explain.

PRACTICE

Write the fraction for the shaded part of each shape.

1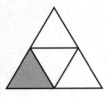

$\dfrac{\square}{4}$ ← shaded part
← equal parts

2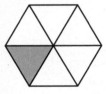

$\dfrac{\square}{\square}$

Model each fraction.

3 $\dfrac{1}{3}$

4 $\dfrac{1}{8}$

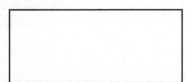

Write the fraction.

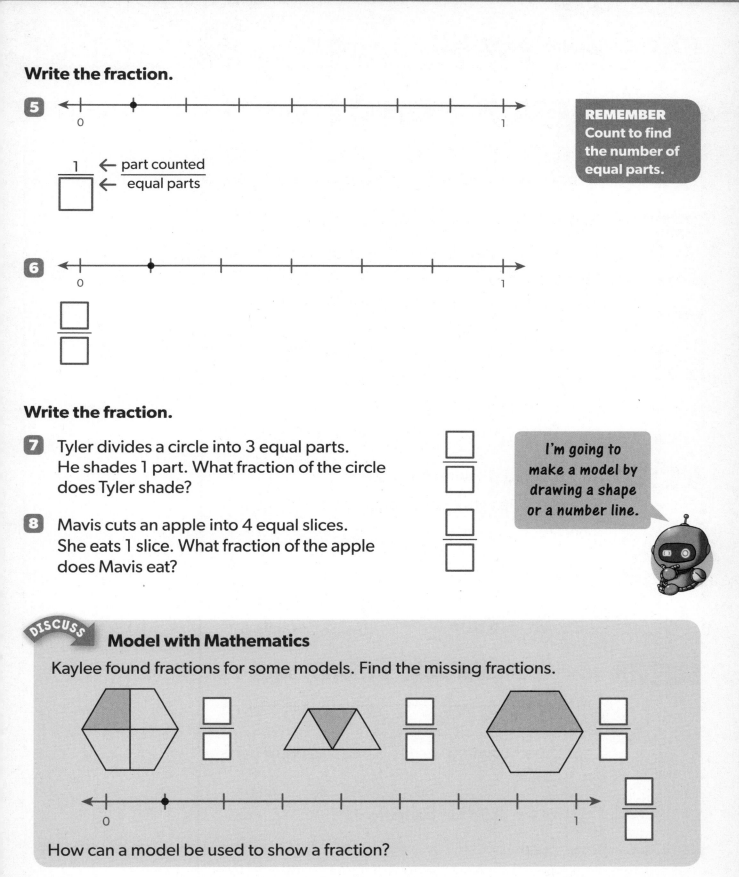

5

0   1

$\frac{1}{\boxed{}}$ ← part counted
    ← equal parts

> **REMEMBER**
> Count to find
> the number of
> equal parts.

6

0   1

$\frac{\boxed{}}{\boxed{}}$

Write the fraction.

7 Tyler divides a circle into 3 equal parts.
He shades 1 part. What fraction of the circle
does Tyler shade?

$\frac{\boxed{}}{\boxed{}}$

8 Mavis cuts an apple into 4 equal slices.
She eats 1 slice. What fraction of the apple
does Mavis eat?

$\frac{\boxed{}}{\boxed{}}$

> I'm going to
> make a model by
> drawing a shape
> or a number line.

DISCUSS **Model with Mathematics**

Kaylee found fractions for some models. Find the missing fractions.

$\frac{\boxed{}}{\boxed{}}$ $\frac{\boxed{}}{\boxed{}}$ $\frac{\boxed{}}{\boxed{}}$

0   1

$\frac{\boxed{}}{\boxed{}}$

How can a model be used to show a fraction?

PROBLEM SOLVING

PIZZA FRACTIONS

READ Mr. Hill makes a pizza. He cuts the pizza into 8 equal slices. 1 slice has pepperoni. What fraction of the pizza has pepperoni?

PLAN • What is the problem asking you to find?

You need to find the fraction of the pizza that has _____.

• What do you need to know to solve the problem?

How many equal slices? _____

How many slices have pepperoni? _____

• How can you show the fraction?

You can use a fraction model or a number line.

SOLVE Make a model. Write the fraction.

Draw a circle with _____ equal parts.

Shade _____ part.

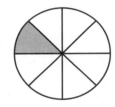

_____ shaded part   _____ equal parts

CHECK Model the fraction another way. Use a number line.

0   1

_____ part counted   _____ equal parts

 of the pizza has pepperoni.

I remember! I need to find equal parts.

PRACTICE

Use the problem-solving steps to help you.

1 Chloe cuts a loaf of bread into 8 equal slices. She gives 1 slice to her friend. What fraction of the bread does Chloe give to her friend?

CHECKLIST
- [ ] READ
- [ ] PLAN
- [ ] SOLVE
- [ ] CHECK

2 A graham cracker has 6 equal pieces. Matthew eats 1 piece. What fraction of the graham cracker does he eat?

CHECKLIST
- [ ] READ
- [ ] PLAN
- [ ] SOLVE
- [ ] CHECK

3 Kuri divides her paper into 4 equal sections. Then she makes 1 section red. What fraction of the paper is colored red?

CHECKLIST
- [ ] READ
- [ ] PLAN
- [ ] SOLVE
- [ ] CHECK

Understanding Fractions

PLUG IN Unit Fractions Using Shapes

A whole can be divided into any number of equal parts.

The circle is divided into halves. **One-half** of the circle is shaded. 1 of 2 equal parts is shaded.

The circle is divided into thirds. **One-third** of the circle is shaded.

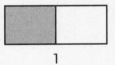

The circle is divided into fourths.

I see! The fraction is $\frac{1}{2}$.

I get it! 1 of 3 equal parts is shaded, so the fraction is $\frac{1}{3}$.

Words to Know

one-half
1 of 2 equal parts

$\frac{1}{2}$

one-third
1 of 3 equal parts

$\frac{1}{3}$

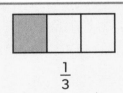

DISCUSS In the fraction $\frac{1}{3}$, which is the denominator? What does it tell us?

A You can count to find the shaded parts of a whole.

 DO

1. How many shaded parts?
2. How many parts in all?
3. Write the fraction.

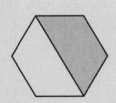

____1____ shaded part

_____ equal parts

fraction $\dfrac{\square}{\square}$

Be careful! The top number tells how many parts are shaded.

B You can find a fraction for a shaded part of a whole.

DO

1 How many shaded parts?

2 How many equal parts in all?

3 Write the fraction.

$$\frac{\square}{\square}$$

C You can make your own fraction model.

DO

1 Shade one part.

2 Count the equal parts.

3 Write the fraction for the shaded part.

$$\frac{\square}{\square}$$

PRACTICE

Write the fraction for the shaded part.

1

_____1____ shaded part

_____ equal parts

fraction $\dfrac{\square}{\square}$

2

$$\dfrac{\square}{\square}$$

Shade one part. Write the fraction for the shaded part.

3

$$\dfrac{\square}{\square}$$

Unit Fractions Using a Number Line

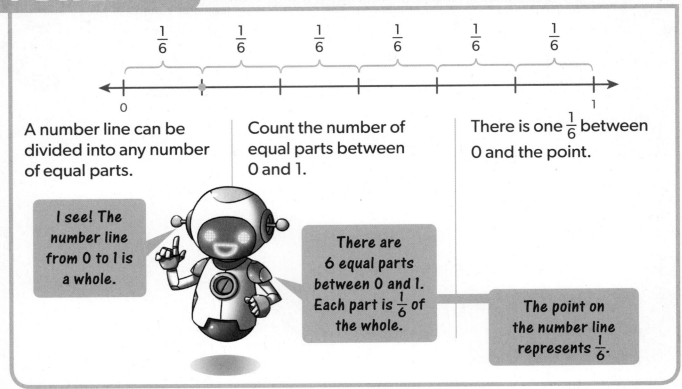

A number line can be divided into any number of equal parts.

Count the number of equal parts between 0 and 1.

There is one $\frac{1}{6}$ between 0 and the point.

I see! The number line from 0 to 1 is a whole.

There are 6 equal parts between 0 and 1. Each part is $\frac{1}{6}$ of the whole.

The point on the number line represents $\frac{1}{6}$.

DISCUSS Suppose you are using a number line to model fractions. How do you know which number to use as the denominator?

A You can model a fraction on a number line.

DO

❶ Count the equal parts between 0 and 1.

❷ Count the parts between 0 and the point.

❸ Write the fraction.

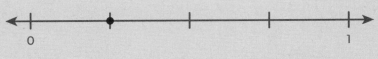

☐ ← number of parts between 0 and the point

☐ ← number of equal parts

B You can model a fraction on a number line.

The number line is divided into equal parts.

DO

Draw a point on the number line to show the fraction $\frac{1}{8}$.

1 Count the number of equal parts. Make sure it is the same as the bottom number.

2 Look at the top number. Count that many from 0.

3 Place a point.

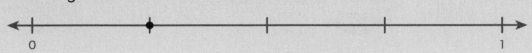

DISCUSS

Ryan drew this number line. He says the point on the number line represents $\frac{1}{5}$. What can you tell Ryan about his work?

PRACTICE

Write the fraction for the point on the number line.

1

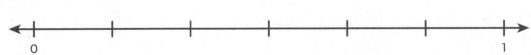

☐ ← number of parts between 0 and the point

─────

☐ ← number of equal parts

Draw a point on the number line to show the fraction.

2 $\frac{1}{6}$

Understanding Fractions

The rectangle is divided into equal parts.

Each shaded part is $\frac{1}{3}$ of the whole.

The fraction $\frac{2}{3}$ can also be shown on a number line.

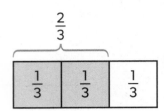

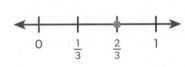

There are 3 equal parts and 2 parts are shaded.

The fraction for the shaded part is $\frac{2}{3}$.

I get it! There are two $\frac{1}{3}$s between 0 and the point. So the point represents $\frac{2}{3}$.

 DISCUSS What do the numerator and denominator of a fraction tell you?

LESSON LINK

PLUG IN	POWER UP	GO!

A fraction can name an equal part of a shape.

1 part of 3 equal parts

$\frac{1}{3}$ is shaded

A fraction can name a point on a number line.

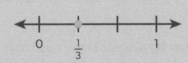

The dot shows where $\frac{1}{3}$ is on a number line.

I get it! A fraction names parts of a whole.

WORK TOGETHER

Draw a number line to show $\frac{6}{8}$.

- There are 8 equal parts between 0 and 1.
- There are six $\frac{1}{8}$s between 0 and the point.
- The point shows the fraction $\frac{6}{8}$.

A Draw a number line to show the fraction.

DO Model the fraction $\frac{2}{3}$.

1. Look at the denominator. There are 3 equal parts.

2. Draw the tic marks to show 3 equal parts.

3. Look at the numerator. There are two $\frac{1}{3}$s between 0 and the point.

4. Draw a point at $\frac{2}{3}$.

B Draw a number line to show the fraction.

DO Model the fraction $\frac{3}{6}$.

1. The denominator shows there are 6 equal parts.

2. Draw the tic marks to show the equal parts.

3. There are three $\frac{1}{6}$s between 0 and the point.

4. Draw a point at $\frac{3}{6}$.

DISCUSS Sydney wants to show the fraction $\frac{3}{8}$ on a number line. She says she will divide the number line into 3 equal parts. Is Sydney correct? Explain.

PRACTICE

Write the fraction for the shaded parts.

1
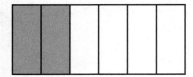

$$\frac{2}{\boxed{}}$$

2
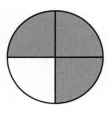

$$\frac{\boxed{}}{\boxed{}}$$

Shade the figure to show the fraction.

3 $\frac{5}{8}$

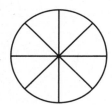

4 $\frac{7}{8}$

Write the fraction for the point on the number line.

5

$$\frac{4}{\square}$$

> **REMEMBER**
> Count to find the number of parts.

6

$$\frac{\square}{\square}$$

Solve.

7 Francisco divides a rectangle into 6 equal parts. He shades 5 parts. What fraction of the rectangle did Francisco shade?

$$\frac{\square}{\square}$$

> I can use a number line to find the fraction.

8 Abigail cuts a pizza into 8 equal slices. She eats 2 slices. What fraction of the pizza did Abigail eat?

$$\frac{\square}{\square}$$

DISCUSS

Model with Mathematics

Jack found fractions for some models. Find the missing fractions.

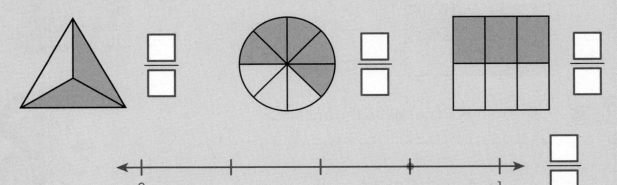

How can a model be used to show a fraction? Write the fractions for the shaded parts.

PROBLEM SOLVING

FABRIC FRACTIONS

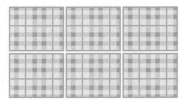

READ Mrs. Bell cuts this fabric into 6 equal pieces. She uses 5 of the pieces to make a quilt. What fraction of the fabric does Mrs. Bell use?

PLAN • What is the problem asking you to find?

You need to find the _____ of the fabric that Mrs. Bell uses.

• What do you need to know to solve the problem?

How many equal pieces in all? _____

How many pieces are used? _____

• What can you use to show the fraction?

You can use a fraction model or a number line.

SOLVE Make a model. Write the fraction.

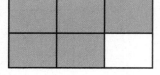

_____ shaded parts

_____ equal parts

□
─
□

> I get it! If my work is correct, my fractions will be the same.

CHECK Use a number line. Write the fraction.

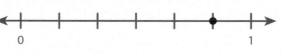

0   1

_____ parts from 0 to the point

_____ equal parts

□
─
□

Mrs. Bell used □/□ of the fabric.

PRACTICE

Use the problem-solving steps to help you.

I remember! I need to find equal parts.

1 Hailey divides a circle into 3 equal parts. Then she colors 2 parts green. What fraction of the circle is colored green?

CHECKLIST
- [ ] READ
- [ ] PLAN
- [ ] SOLVE
- [ ] CHECK

2 Nathan cuts a cake into 8 equal slices. He gives 7 slices to his friends. What fraction of the cake does Nathan give to his friends?

CHECKLIST
- [ ] READ
- [ ] PLAN
- [ ] SOLVE
- [ ] CHECK

3 A graham cracker is broken into 6 equal pieces. Grace, Taylor, and Nicolas each eat 1 piece. What fraction of the graham cracker do they eat?

CHECKLIST
- [ ] READ
- [ ] PLAN
- [ ] SOLVE
- [ ] CHECK

Equivalent Fractions

PLUG IN Understanding Fractions

The rectangle is divided into equal parts. The total number of equal parts is the **denominator**.

$\frac{1}{4}$	$\frac{1}{4}$	$\frac{1}{4}$	$\frac{1}{4}$

The number of shaded parts is the **numerator**.

$\frac{1}{4}$	$\frac{1}{4}$	$\frac{1}{4}$	$\frac{1}{4}$

Each shaded part is $\frac{1}{4}$ of the whole. The **fraction** for the shaded part is $\frac{2}{4}$.

$\frac{2}{4}$

$\frac{1}{4}$	$\frac{1}{4}$	$\frac{1}{4}$	$\frac{1}{4}$

> There are 4 equal parts.

> 2 parts are shaded.

> I see! There are 4 equal parts and 2 parts are shaded.

Words to Know

denominator
the number of equal parts

numerator
the number of parts being counted

fraction
names equal parts of a whole

DISCUSS When writing a fraction, how do you know which number to use for the denominator and which number to use for the numerator?

A You can write a fraction to name the shaded parts of a whole.

DO

1. How many shaded parts?
2. How many equal parts in all?
3. Write the fraction.

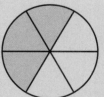

___3___ shaded parts

_____ equal parts

fraction

B You can write a fraction to name the shaded parts of a whole.

DO

1. Count the number of shaded parts. This is the numerator.

2. Count the total number of equal parts. This is the denominator.

3. Write the fraction.

> Be careful! The numerator is the top number in the fraction.

$$\frac{\square}{\square}$$

C You can make your own fraction models.

DO Model $\frac{1}{2}$.

1. Draw a circle to show 1 whole.

2. The denominator is 2. Divide the circle into 2 equal parts.

3. The numerator is 1. Shade 1 part.

PRACTICE

Write a fraction to name the shaded parts.

1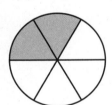

___2___ shaded parts

_____ equal parts

$$\frac{\square}{\square}$$

2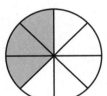

$$\frac{\square}{\square}$$

Draw a fraction model for $\frac{1}{3}$.

3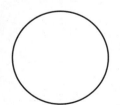

Fractions on a Number Line

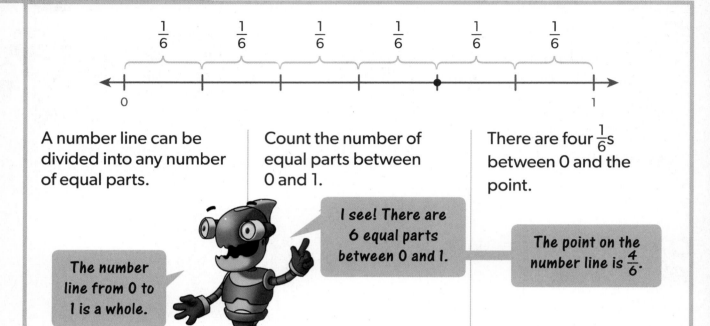

A number line can be divided into any number of equal parts.

Count the number of equal parts between 0 and 1.

There are four $\frac{1}{6}$s between 0 and the point.

The number line from 0 to 1 is a whole.

I see! There are 6 equal parts between 0 and 1.

The point on the number line is $\frac{4}{6}$.

DISCUSS

When using a number line to model fractions, how do you know which number to use as the numerator?

A You can write a fraction to name a point on a number line.

DO

1. Look at the number line. Count the total number of equal parts between 0 and 1.

2. Count the number of parts between 0 and the point.

3. Write the fraction.

The total number of equal parts is ___**4**___.

The number line is divided into _____.

There are _____ $\frac{1}{4}$s between 0 and the point.

☐

☐

B You can make a number line to show a fraction.

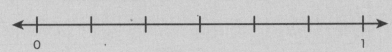

DO Model $\frac{3}{6}$.

❶ Use the denominator to find the total number of equal parts between 0 and 1.

The number line will have ___**6**___ equal parts.

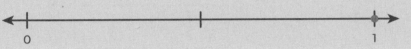

❷ Draw the number line.

There will be _____ $\frac{1}{6}$s between 0 and the point.

❸ Use the numerator to find the number of parts between 0 and the point.

❹ Draw the point on the number line.

DISCUSS Soo Ha drew this number line. She says the point on the number line represents $\frac{2}{3}$. What can you tell Soo Ha about her work?

PRACTICE

Write a fraction for the point on the number line.

1

Model the fraction $\frac{5}{8}$ on the number line.

2

A rectangle can be divided into equal parts.

| $\frac{1}{3}$ | $\frac{1}{3}$ | $\frac{1}{3}$ |

The number of equal parts can be different.

| $\frac{1}{6}$ | $\frac{1}{6}$ | $\frac{1}{6}$ | $\frac{1}{6}$ | $\frac{1}{6}$ | $\frac{1}{6}$ |

The shaded part of each model is the same size. The models show **equivalent fractions**.

| $\frac{1}{3}$ | $\frac{1}{3}$ | $\frac{1}{3}$ |

| $\frac{1}{6}$ | $\frac{1}{6}$ | $\frac{1}{6}$ | $\frac{1}{6}$ | $\frac{1}{6}$ | $\frac{1}{6}$ |

Each of the parts is $\frac{1}{3}$ of the whole.

The rectangle is the same size, but each of the parts is $\frac{1}{6}$ of the whole.

I see! Both fractions name the same amount.

Words to Know

equivalent fractions
two or more fractions that name the same amount

| $\frac{1}{2}$ | $\frac{1}{2}$ |

| $\frac{1}{4}$ | $\frac{1}{4}$ | $\frac{1}{4}$ | $\frac{1}{4}$ |

DISCUSS Why are the numbers in equivalent fractions not the same?

LESSON LINK

| **PLUG IN** | **POWER UP** | **GO!** |

PLUG IN

A fraction names part of a whole.

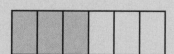

$\frac{3}{6}$ of the rectangle is shaded.

POWER UP

A number line can show parts of a whole.

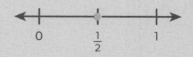

0    $\frac{1}{2}$ 1

The point is at $\frac{1}{2}$.

GO!

I see! Two or more equivalent fractions can name the same part of the whole.

WORK TOGETHER

Fold a sheet of paper to show fractions.

- Fold a sheet of paper in thirds.
- Color $\frac{1}{3}$ of the paper.
- Fold the paper in half. Now $\frac{2}{6}$ of the paper is colored.

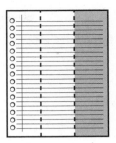 

$\frac{1}{3}$ shaded $\frac{2}{6}$ shaded

I see! $\frac{1}{3}$ and $\frac{2}{6}$ name the same amount. They are equivalent.

A Fold a piece of paper to model a fraction.

DO Model $\frac{1}{2}$.

1. Fold the sheet of paper in half. Fold from left to right.
2. Color one-half of the paper.
3. Write the fraction for the colored part of the paper.

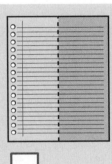

B Use the same piece of paper to model an equivalent fraction.

DO Model $\frac{2}{4}$.

1. Fold the sheet of paper in half again. Fold from top to bottom.
2. Write the fraction for the colored part of the paper.

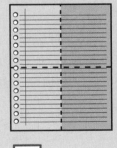

I can model equivalent fractions.

 DISCUSS Look at two equivalent fractions such as $\frac{1}{2}$ and $\frac{2}{4}$. Why does the numerator get bigger when the denominator gets bigger?

PRACTICE

Are the fractions equivalent? Write *yes* or *no*.

1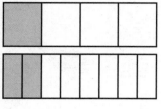

___yes___

2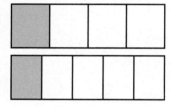

_____

3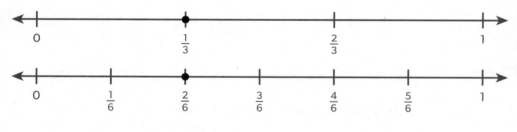

_____

4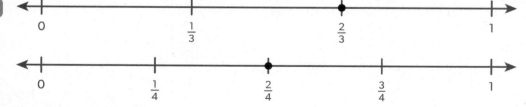

_____

Fill in the numerators to write equivalent fractions.

5

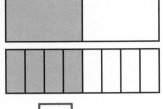

$$\frac{1}{2} = \frac{\square}{8}$$

6

$$\frac{3}{6} = \frac{\square}{8}$$

Write the fractions.

7 Write a fraction that is equivalent to $\frac{1}{4}$.

8 Write a fraction that is equivalent to $\frac{2}{3}$.

I'm going to make a model by drawing a shape or a number line.

DISCUSS **Model with Mathematics**

Noah modeled two fractions. He says the fractions are equivalent. Do you agree or disagree?

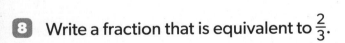

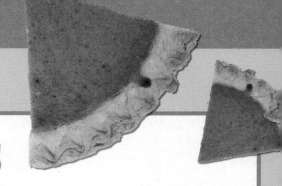

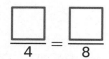

PROBLEM SOLVING

PIE FRACTIONS

READ Lauren and Jackson each baked a pie. Their pies were the same size. Lauren gave away $\frac{2}{4}$ of her pie. Jackson gave away $\frac{4}{8}$ of his pie. Are these fractions equivalent?

PLAN
- What is the problem asking you to find?

    You need to find if the fractions are _____.

- What do you need to know to solve the problem?

    What fractions of pie were given away? _____ and _____

- How can you show both fractions?

    You can use fraction models or number lines.

SOLVE Make a model.

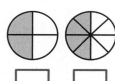

$$\frac{\square}{4} = \frac{\square}{8}$$

CHECK Model the fractions another way. Use a number line.

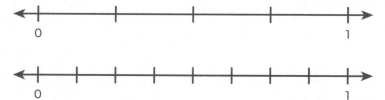

$$\frac{\square}{4} = \frac{\square}{8}$$

The fractions $\frac{2}{4}$ and $\frac{4}{8}$ _____ equivalent.

I get it! If my work is correct, my fractions will show the same size.

PRACTICE

Use the problem-solving steps to help you.

1 Percy shades $\frac{3}{4}$ of his paper red. Madison has a paper that is the same size as Percy's paper. Madison shades $\frac{6}{8}$ of her paper red. Are the fractions $\frac{3}{4}$ and $\frac{6}{8}$ equivalent?

CHECKLIST
- [ ] READ
- [ ] PLAN
- [ ] SOLVE
- [ ] CHECK

2 Emily paints $\frac{1}{2}$ of her wall blue. Zachary is painting a wall that is the same size as Emily's wall. Zachary paints $\frac{2}{3}$ of his wall. Are the fractions $\frac{1}{2}$ and $\frac{2}{3}$ equivalent?

CHECKLIST
- [ ] READ
- [ ] PLAN
- [ ] SOLVE
- [ ] CHECK

3 Alyssa eats $\frac{3}{6}$ of her personal size pizza. Caden eats $\frac{1}{2}$ of his personal size pizza. Did Alyssa and Caden eat the same amount of pizza?

CHECKLIST
- [ ] READ
- [ ] PLAN
- [ ] SOLVE
- [ ] CHECK

Comparing Fractions

PLUG IN · Comparing Whole Numbers

You can use words or symbols to compare numbers.

Compare the digits from left to right.

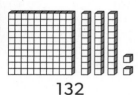
132

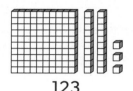
123

132 is **greater than** 123

132 > 123

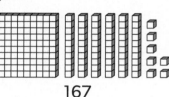
167

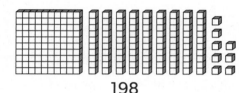
198

167 is **less than** 198

167 < 198

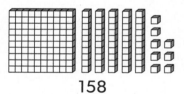
158

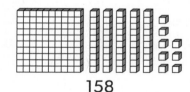
158

158 is **equal to** 158

158 = 158

Words to Know

greater than	**less than**	**equal to**
one number has more than another number	one number has fewer than another number	both numbers are the same
186 > 168	168 < 186	186 = 186

DISCUSS How do you know 398 is greater than 298?

A You can use words or symbols to compare numbers.

 Compare 137 and 139.

 Be careful! Always compare from left to right.

1 Compare hundreds.

2 Compare tens.

3 Compare ones.

4 Write *greater than* (>), *less than* (<), or *equal to* (=).

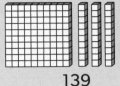

137   139

137 is _____ 139. 137 _____ 139

B You can use a place-value chart to help compare numbers.

 Compare 219 and 213.

1 Compare hundreds.

2 Compare tens.

3 Compare ones.

4 Write >, <, or =.

Hundreds	Tens	Ones
2	1	9
2	1	3

219 ◯ 213

PRACTICE

Compare the numbers. Write >, <, or =.

1

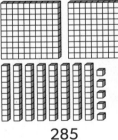

285

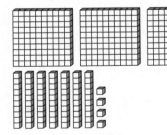

374

285 ◯ 374

Use the place-value chart to compare the numbers. Use >, <, or =.

2

Hundreds	Tens	Ones
3	8	5
2	8	5

385 ◯ 285

Understanding Fractions

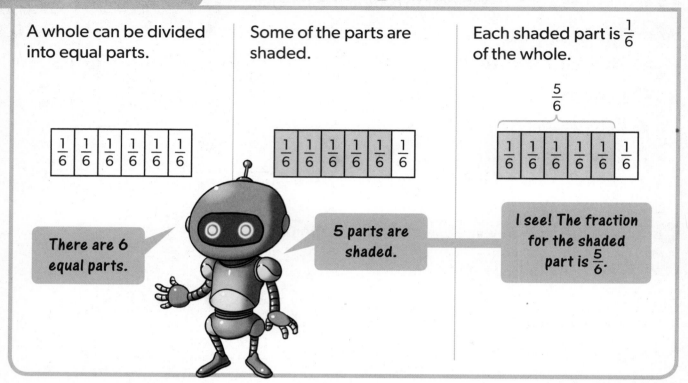

A whole can be divided into equal parts.

There are 6 equal parts.

Some of the parts are shaded.

5 parts are shaded.

Each shaded part is $\frac{1}{6}$ of the whole.

$\frac{5}{6}$

I see! The fraction for the shaded part is $\frac{5}{6}$.

DISCUSS What does it mean to say a rectangle models the fraction $\frac{5}{6}$?

A You can write a fraction for the shaded parts of a whole.

DO

1. Count the shaded parts.
2. Count all the equal parts.
3. Write the fraction for the shaded parts.

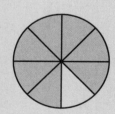

$\dfrac{7}{\boxed{}}$

Be careful! The denominator tells how many equal parts in all.

B You can find a fraction for the shaded parts of a whole.

❶ Count the shaded parts.

❷ Count the equal parts.

❸ Write the fraction for the shaded parts.

$$\frac{\square}{8}$$

 Riley says the model represents $\frac{6}{4}$. What can you tell Riley about her work?

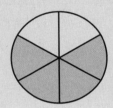

PRACTICE

You can count to find the shaded parts of a whole.

 Write the fraction for the shaded parts.

$$\frac{\square}{\square}$$

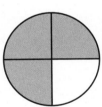

 Write the fraction for the shaded parts.

$$\frac{\square}{\square}$$

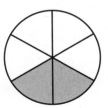

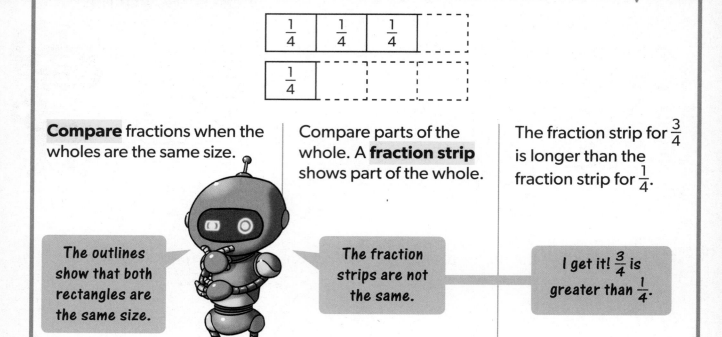

| $\frac{1}{4}$ | $\frac{1}{4}$ | $\frac{1}{4}$ | |
| $\frac{1}{4}$ | | | |

Compare fractions when the wholes are the same size.

Compare parts of the whole. A **fraction strip** shows part of the whole.

The fraction strip for $\frac{3}{4}$ is longer than the fraction strip for $\frac{1}{4}$.

The outlines show that both rectangles are the same size.

The fraction strips are not the same.

I get it! $\frac{3}{4}$ is greater than $\frac{1}{4}$.

Words to Know

compare
to find which of two values is greater

fraction strip
a model of a fraction of a whole

DISCUSS What happens to the size of a fraction strip as the denominator gets larger if the numerator stays the same? Explain.

LESSON LINK

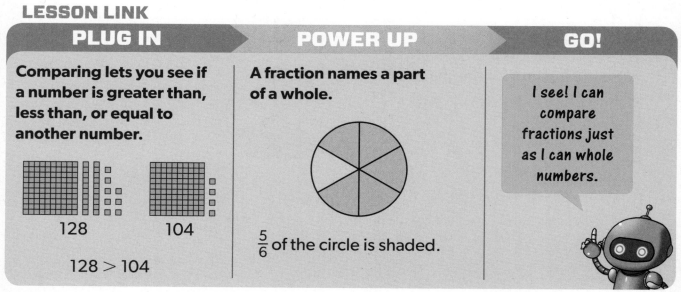

| PLUG IN | POWER UP | GO! |

Comparing lets you see if a number is greater than, less than, or equal to another number.

128   104

128 > 104

A fraction names a part of a whole.

$\frac{5}{6}$ of the circle is shaded.

I see! I can compare fractions just as I can whole numbers.

WORK TOGETHER

Draw fraction models to compare fractions.

I see! $\frac{4}{6}$ is greater than $\frac{2}{6}$.

- This model shows $\frac{4}{6}$ shaded.
- It also shows $\frac{2}{6}$ not shaded.
- $\frac{4}{6}$ covers more of the rectangle than $\frac{2}{6}$.
- $\frac{4}{6}$ is greater than $\frac{2}{6}$.

A Draw a fraction model to compare.

DO Model $\frac{3}{4}$.

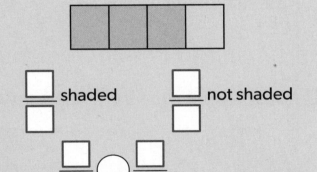

1. Draw a rectangle. Divide it into 4 equal parts. Shade 3 parts.

2. Write fractions for both the shaded parts and the part not shaded.

3. Compare the fractions. Write >, <, or =.

☐ / ☐ shaded   ☐ / ☐ not shaded

☐/☐ ◯ ☐/☐

B Compare fraction models.

DO Model $\frac{1}{4}$ and $\frac{2}{4}$.

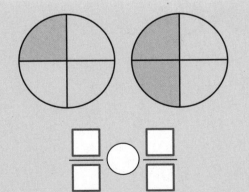

1. Draw two circles. Make sure they are both the same size.

2. Divide one circle into 4 equal parts. Shade 1 part.

3. Divide the other circle into 4 equal parts. Shade 2 parts.

4. Compare the fractions.

☐/☐ ◯ ☐/☐

DISCUSS Caleb wants to compare $\frac{1}{3}$ and $\frac{2}{3}$.

Which numbers does he need to compare? Explain.

$\frac{1}{3}$ ◯ $\frac{2}{3}$

PRACTICE

Compare the fractions.

1 Write the lesser fraction.

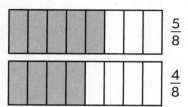

$\frac{5}{8}$

$\frac{4}{8}$

$\frac{\square}{8}$ is the lesser fraction.

2 Write the greater fraction.

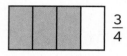
$\frac{3}{4}$

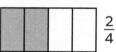
$\frac{2}{4}$

The greater fraction is $\frac{\square}{\square}$.

3 Write >, <, or =.

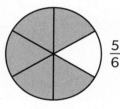
$\frac{5}{6}$

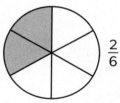
$\frac{2}{6}$

$\frac{5}{6} \bigcirc \frac{2}{6}$

4 Write >, <, or =.

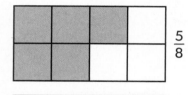
$\frac{5}{8}$

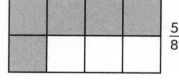
$\frac{5}{8}$

$\frac{5}{8} \bigcirc \frac{5}{8}$

5 Write >, <, or =.

$\frac{6}{8} \bigcirc \frac{2}{8}$

Draw a model for each fraction. Compare. Write >, <, or =.

6 $\frac{2}{4}$ and $\frac{1}{4}$

7 $\frac{3}{6}$ and $\frac{4}{6}$

$\frac{2}{4}\bigcirc\frac{1}{4}$

$\frac{3}{6}\bigcirc\frac{4}{6}$

I can use fraction strips to compare the fractions.

Compare the fractions.

8 Maria has $\frac{2}{3}$ cup of raisins and Logan has $\frac{1}{3}$ cup of raisins. Who has more raisins? _____

9 Isabella ran $\frac{1}{6}$ of a mile. Samantha ran $\frac{5}{6}$ of a mile. Which girl ran farther? _____

DISCUSS **Model with Mathematics**

Dylan baked an apple pie and a blueberry pie. The pies were the same size. He gave away $\frac{3}{4}$ of the apple pie and $\frac{2}{4}$ of the blueberry pie. He tells his friend that he gave away more of the blueberry pie. Is Dylan correct?

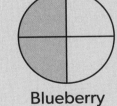

Apple   Blueberry

REMEMBER
Look at the denominators first.

PROBLEM SOLVING

SANDWICH COMPARISONS

READ   Connor ate $\frac{3}{4}$ of his sandwich. Ethan ate $\frac{2}{4}$ of his sandwich. Which boy ate more of his sandwich?

PLAN

• What is the problem asking you to find?

     You need to find out which boy ate _____ of his sandwich.

• What do you need to know to solve the problem?

     What fraction of his sandwich did Connor eat? _____

     What fraction of his sandwich did Ethan eat? _____

• How can you show the comparison?

     You can use fraction strips or models.

SOLVE

• Compare the denominators. Then compare the numerators.

     The denominators are the _____.

     The numerators are _____.

• Compare the fractions by comparing the numerators.

     _____ is greater than _____ , so $\frac{3}{4}$ is _____ than $\frac{2}{4}$.

> I get it! If my work is correct, my models will prove my answer.

CHECK   Shade the models to check.

Shade $\frac{3}{4}$.

Shade $\frac{2}{4}$.

_____ ate more of his sandwich.

PRACTICE

Use the problem-solving steps to help you.

1 Jacob and Jose have papers that are the same size. Jacob shaded $\frac{2}{8}$ of his paper blue. Jose shaded $\frac{7}{8}$ of his paper blue. Who shaded more of his paper?

CHECKLIST
- [ ] READ
- [ ] PLAN
- [ ] SOLVE
- [ ] CHECK

2 Alexandra practices piano for $\frac{1}{4}$ of an hour. Melissa practices piano for $\frac{2}{4}$ of an hour. Which girl practices longer?

CHECKLIST
- [ ] READ
- [ ] PLAN
- [ ] SOLVE
- [ ] CHECK

3 Mr. Adams picked apples. $\frac{2}{3}$ of the apples were green and $\frac{1}{3}$ of the apples were red. Did Mr. Adams pick more green or red apples?

CHECKLIST
- [ ] READ
- [ ] PLAN
- [ ] SOLVE
- [ ] CHECK

5 Adding Whole Numbers

PLUG IN Addition with Regrouping

When you **add** whole numbers, sometimes you need to **regroup**.

4③ + 2⑨

> There are more than 10 ones.

Write the problem in a **place-value chart**. Add the ones.

	Tens	Ones
	1	
	4	3
+	2	9
		2

> There are 12 ones. Regroup 12 ones as 1 ten and 2 ones.

Add the tens.

	Tens	Ones
	1	
	4	3
+	2	9
	7	2

> I see! There are 7 tens and 2 ones, so 43 + 29 = 72.

Words to Know

add
to put together or join
3 + 5 = 8

regroup
to form into a new group of equal value

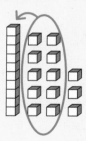

13 ones = 1 ten 3 ones

place-value chart
a chart that shows the value of each digit of a number

Tens	Ones
5	6

5 tens
6 ones

DISCUSS Why do you need to regroup to add 45 and 27?

A You can add using a place-value chart.

 DO Add 19 + 32.

① Write the problem in a place-value chart.

② Add the ones. Regroup if needed.

③ Add the tens.

④ Write the sum.

	Tens	Ones
	1	9
+	3	2

There are _____ tens and _____ one.

The sum is _____.

B You can add by lining up tens and ones.

DO Add 24 + 18.

① Line up the numbers by tens and ones.

② Add the ones. Regroup if needed.

③ Add the tens.

④ Find the sum.

$$\begin{array}{cc} 2 & 4 \\ + \ 1 & 8 \\ \hline \square & \square \end{array}$$

There are _____ tens and _____ ones.

The sum is _____.

PRACTICE

Use the place-value charts. Add to find the sums.

1

	Tens	Ones
	3	8
+	2	7

2

	Tens	Ones
	4	2
+	1	8

Line up the numbers by tens and ones. Add to find the sums.

3 61 + 29

$$\begin{array}{cc} 6 & 1 \\ + \ \square & \square \\ \hline \square & \square \end{array}$$

4 35 + 26

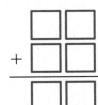

POWER UP — Adding Greater Numbers

Adding 3-digit numbers is a lot like adding 2-digit numbers.

128 + 161

Use a place-value chart to find the sum.

	Hundreds	Tens	Ones
	1	2	8
+	1	6	1

Add the ones. Then the tens. Then the hundreds.

	Hundreds	Tens	Ones
	1	2	8
+	1	6	1
	2	8	9

The place values of the numerals are hundreds, tens, and ones.

I can start by adding the ones.

Got it! There are 2 hundreds, 8 tens, and 9 ones. The sum is 289.

DISCUSS   Why is it important to start adding at the ones place?

A   You can use a place-value chart to add 3-digit numbers.

 DO   Add 381 + 115.

1 Write the problem in a place-value chart.

2 Add numbers in each place. Start with ones. Regroup if needed.

3 Write the sum.

	Hundreds	Tens	Ones
	3	8	1
+	1	1	5

There are _____ hundreds, _____ tens,

and _____ ones.

The sum is _____.

B You can add 3-digit numbers by lining up hundreds, tens, and ones.

Add 324 + 371.

❶ Line up the numbers.

❷ Add numbers in each place. Start with ones. Regroup if needed.

❸ Write the sum.

$$\begin{array}{ccc} 3 & 2 & 4 \\ + \ 3 & 7 & 1 \\ \hline \square & \square & 5 \end{array}$$

There are _____ hundreds, _____ tens,

and _____ ones.

The sum is _____.

Michael solved the addition problem 174 + 222 as shown below.

$$\begin{array}{r} 174 \\ + \ 222 \\ \hline 1{,}962 \end{array}$$

What can you tell him about his work?

PRACTICE

Use the place-value charts. Add to find the sums.

1

	Hundreds	Tens	Ones
	4	2	9
+	2	3	0

2

	Hundreds	Tens	Ones
	5	0	7
+	3	6	1

Line up the numbers. Add to find the sums.

3 134 + 215

4 440 + 328

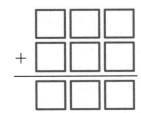

Adding Whole Numbers

Sometimes you need to regroup when adding 3-digit numbers.

$$4\ 7\,②+1\ 1\,⑨$$

	Hundreds	Tens	Ones
		1	
	4	7	2
+	1	1	9
			1

There are 5 hundreds, 9 tens, and 1 one.

	Hundreds	Tens	Ones
		1	
	4	7	2
+	1	1	9
	5	9	1

I see! There are 11 ones, so I need to regroup 11 ones as 1 ten and 1 one.

So, the sum is 591.

 DISCUSS

What place do you need to regroup to add 581 + 238? Explain.

LESSON LINK

PLUG IN	POWER UP	GO!
Sometimes you need to regroup to add 2-digit numbers.	Addition with 3-digit numbers works a lot like addition with 2-digit numbers.	I get it! I can use what I know about regrouping to help me add greater numbers.

PLUG IN

Sometimes you need to regroup to add 2-digit numbers.

$$\begin{array}{r} 1\ \ \\ 59 \\ +34 \\ \hline 93 \end{array}$$

POWER UP

Addition with 3-digit numbers works a lot like addition with 2-digit numbers.

$$\begin{array}{r} 124 \\ +610 \\ \hline 734 \end{array}$$

GO!

I get it! I can use what I know about regrouping to help me add greater numbers.

WORK TOGETHER

Use place-value models to show addition.

- Show 129 + 136.

- Group by place value. Regroup if needed.

- There are 2 hundreds, 6 tens, and 5 ones.

- The sum is 265.

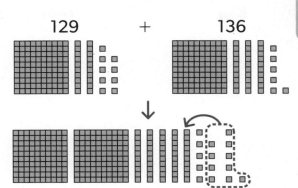

129 + 136

I can use real objects to show joining groups.

Place-value models can be found on p. 213.

A Use place-value models.

 Add 156 + 128.

① Show 156 + 128 with models.

② Group all hundreds, all tens, and all ones.

③ Regroup if needed.

④ Find the sum.

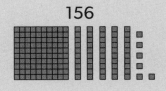

156

128

156 + 128 = _____

B You can use a place-value chart to add 3-digit numbers.

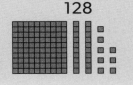 Add 135 + 172.

① Add ones. Regroup if needed.

② Add tens. Regroup if needed.

③ Add hundreds.

④ Find the sum.

	Hundreds	Tens	Ones
	1	3	5
+	1	7	2

There are _____ hundreds, _____ tens,

and _____ ones. The sum is _____.

 Traci wants to check her answer to 391 + 158 = 449.

How can she check her answer? Is the answer correct?

PRACTICE

Do you need to regroup? Write *yes* or *no*.

1 2⑧4 + 1②1

_____

HINT
Regroup when there are 10 or more ones or tens.

2 124 + 331

_____

Use the place-value charts. Add to find the sums.

3 263 + 490

	Hundreds	Tens	Ones
	2	6	3
+	4	9	0

The sum is _____.

4 425 + 137

	Hundreds	Tens	Ones
+	☐ ☐	☐	☐
	☐	☐	☐

The sum is _____.

Add to find the sums.

5 378 + 214

```
    3 7 8
+  ☐ ☐ ☐
 ─────────
   ☐ ☐ ☐
```

6 573 + 184

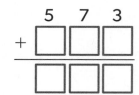

```
    5 7 3
+  ☐ ☐ ☐
 ─────────
   ☐ ☐ ☐
```

REMEMBER
Rewrite the problem and line up the place values if you need to.

Solve.

7 In April, 479 people visited the art museum. In May, 506 people visited the museum. How many people visited the museum in April and May combined? _____

I'm going to use place-value models.

8 Ben read 113 pages in his book. There are 109 more pages in the book. How many pages are in the book? _____

DISCUSS

See the Pattern

Eva wrote some addition sentences. She forgot some of the numbers.

Write the missing numbers.

$5 + \boxed{} = 6$

$50 + 10 = \boxed{}$

$500 + \boxed{} = 600$

What pattern do you see in these addition sentences?

HINT
How does the sum change in each addition sentence?

PROBLEM SOLVING

COLLECTING CANS

READ Mr. Lopez's class collected 212 cans to recycle. Mrs. Wright's class collected 193 cans. How many cans did the classes collect in all?

PLAN • What is the problem asking you to find?

You need to find how many _____ the classes collected in all.

• What do you need to know to solve the problem?

How many cans did Mr. Lopez's class collect? _____

How many cans did Mrs. Wright's class collect? _____

• How can you show the addition?

You can use a place-value chart or place-value models.

SOLVE Use place-value models.

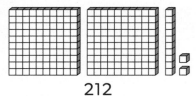
212

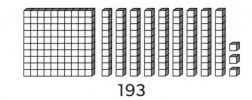
193

$212 + 193 =$ _____

CHECK Use a place-value chart.

	Hundreds	Tens	Ones
	2	1	2
+	1	9	3

The classes collected _____ cans in all.

PRACTICE

Use the problem-solving steps to help you.

1 Aidan's family drove 183 miles on Saturday and 163 miles on Sunday. How many miles did they drive in all?

CHECKLIST
- [ ] READ
- [ ] PLAN
- [ ] SOLVE
- [ ] CHECK

2 There are 125 girls and 117 boys in the third grade. How many students in all are in the third grade?

CHECKLIST
- [ ] READ
- [ ] PLAN
- [ ] SOLVE
- [ ] CHECK

3 A factory makes 139 red chairs and 124 blue chairs. How many chairs does the factory make in all?

CHECKLIST
- [ ] READ
- [ ] PLAN
- [ ] SOLVE
- [ ] CHECK

6 Subtracting Whole Numbers

PLUG IN · Subtract within 100

When you **subtract** whole numbers, sometimes you need to **regroup**.

$$\begin{array}{r} 6\circled{2} \\ -\ 3\circled{8} \end{array}$$

There are not enough ones in 62 to subtract 8 ones.

Use **place-value** models for 62. Regroup 1 ten as 10 ones.

You can break up one of the tens into 10 ones.

Subtract 8 ones. Then subtract 3 tens. Count what is left.

I see! There are 2 tens and 4 ones left, so 62 − 38 = 24.

Words to Know

subtract
to take away or remove

regroup
to form into a new group of equal value

place-value
the value of a digit based on where it is in a number

DISCUSS Why is it important to regroup to subtract 56 − 18?

A You can use a place-value chart to subtract.

DO Subtract 45 − 17.

❶ Write the problem in a place-value chart.

❷ Subtract the ones. Regroup. Write the new tens and ones.

❸ Subtract the tens.

❹ Write the difference.

	Tens	Ones
	4	5
−	1	7

There are _____ tens and _____ ones.

The difference is _____.

B You can subtract by lining up place values without a chart.

DO   Subtract 73 − 39.

1 Line up the numbers by place value.

2 Subtract the ones. Regroup. Write the new tens and ones.

3 Subtract the tens.

4 Write the difference.

$$\begin{array}{r} 7\,3 \\ -\,3\,9 \\ \hline 4 \end{array}$$

There are _____ tens and _____ ones.

The difference is _____.

C You can use addition to check the answer to a subtraction problem.

DO

1 Set up the addition problem.

2 Add the ones. Regroup 14 as 1 ten and 4 ones.

3 Add the tens.

4 Check that the final numbers match.

$$\begin{array}{r} 8\,4 \\ -\,3\,6 \\ \hline 4\,8 \end{array} \qquad \begin{array}{r} 3\,6 \\ +\,4\,8 \\ \hline \end{array}$$

The numbers in the subtraction problem are 84, 36, and 48.

The numbers in the addition problem are

_____, _____ and _____.

PRACTICE

Line up the numbers by tens and ones. Subtract to find the difference. Add to check the answer.

1 25 − 18

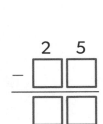
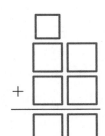

2

$$\begin{array}{r} 7\,3 \\ -\,2\,6 \\ \hline 4\,7 \end{array}$$

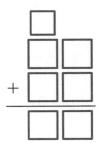

Subtracting Greater Numbers

Subtracting 3-digit numbers is a lot like subtracting 2-digit numbers.

$$653 - 231$$

The place values of each number are hundreds, tens, and ones.

Use place-value models for 653.

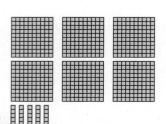

653

There are 6 hundreds, 5 tens, and 3 ones in 653.

To subtract, cross out 1 one, 3 tens, and 2 hundreds. Then count what is left.

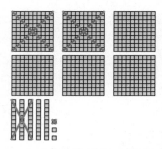

I see! There are 4 hundreds, 2 tens, and 2 ones left, so the difference is 422.

DISCUSS Why is it important to start subtracting with the ones place?

A You can use a place-value chart to subtract 3-digit numbers.

DO Subtract 758 − 420.

① Write the problem in a place-value chart.

② Subtract the numbers in each place.

③ Write the difference.

	Hundreds	Tens	Ones
	7	5	8
−	4	2	0
			8

There are _____ hundreds, _____ tens, and _____ ones.

The difference is _____.

B You also can subtract 3-digit numbers by lining up place values.

 Subtract 679 − 374.

1. Line up the numbers by place value.

2. Subtract the numbers in each place, starting with the ones.

3. Write the difference.

$$
\begin{array}{r}
6\ \ 7\ \ 9 \\
-\ 3\ \ 7\ \ 4 \\
\hline
\boxed{\ }\ \boxed{\ }\ 5
\end{array}
$$

There are _____ hundreds, _____ tens, and _____ ones.

The difference is _____.

DISCUSS Xavier wants to check the answer to his subtraction problem. What can you tell him about checking his answer?

$$
\begin{array}{r}
1\,5\,3 \\
-1\,1\,0 \\
\hline
4\,3
\end{array}
$$

PRACTICE

Use the place-value chart. Subtract to find the difference.

1. 587 − 532

	Hundreds	Tens	Ones
−			

Line up the numbers by place values. Subtract to find the difference.

2. 463 − 241

3. 392 − 250

Sometimes you need to regroup when subtracting 3-digit numbers.

3②9 − 1⑤3

	Hundreds	Tens	Ones
	2 ̶3̶	12 ̶2̶	9
−	1	5	3
		7	6

There are 1 hundred, 7 tens, and 6 ones left.

	Hundreds	Tens	Ones
	2 ̶3̶	12 ̶2̶	9
−	1	5	3
	1	7	6

I see! There are not enough tens to subtract. I can regroup 1 hundred as 10 tens.

So, the difference is 176.

DISCUSS What place values do you have to regroup to subtract 835 − 469? Explain.

LESSON LINK

PLUG IN

Sometimes you need to regroup to subtract 2-digit numbers.

```
  6 13
  7̶3̶
− 5 4
─────
  1 9
```

POWER UP

Subtraction with 3-digit numbers works a lot like subtraction with 2-digit numbers.

```
  5 7 6
− 3 4 2
───────
  2 3 4
```

GO!

I see! I can use what I know about regrouping to help me subtract 3-digit numbers.

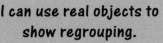

WORK TOGETHER

Use place-value models to show subtraction.

Subtract 342 − 126.

- The model shows 342 − 126.
- Regroup 1 ten as 10 ones.
- Cross out 1 hundred, 2 tens, and 6 ones.
- There are 2 hundreds, 1 ten, and 6 ones left. So, the difference is 216.

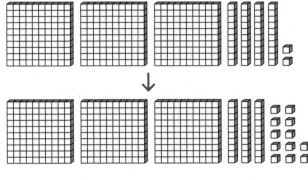

342 − _____ = _____

A Use place-value models.

DO Subtract 368 − 172.

1. Subtract the ones.
2. Regroup 1 hundred as 10 tens. Subtract the tens.
3. Subtract the hundreds.
4. Find the difference.

There are _____ hundreds, _____ tens, and _____ ones.

The difference is _____.

Place-value models can be found on p. 215.

B Use a place-value chart.

DO Subtract 235 − 178.

1. Subtract the ones. Regroup if needed.
2. Subtract the tens. Regroup if needed.
3. Subtract the hundreds.
4. Find the difference.

	Hundreds	Tens	Ones
	2	3	5
−	1	7	8

There are _____ hundreds, _____ tens, and _____ ones.

The difference is _____.

DISCUSS Anna wants to check her answer to 426 − 381 = 35. How can she check her answer? Is her answer correct?

PRACTICE

Do you need to regroup? Write *yes* or *no*.

1 3④8 − 2⑥2

_____

HINT
Regroup when there are not enough tens.

2 195 − 143

_____

Use a place-value chart. Subtract to find the difference.

3 763 − 290

	Hundreds	Tens	Ones
	7	6	3
−	2	9	0
			3

REMEMBER
You need to cross out when you regroup.

The difference is _____.

4 925 − 548

	Hundreds	Tens	Ones
	☐	☐	☐
−	☐	☐	☐
	☐	☐	☐

The difference is _____.

Subtract to find the difference.

5 849 − 562

$$
\begin{array}{ccc}
8 & 4 & 9 \\
- \Box & \Box & \Box \\
\hline
\Box & \Box & \Box
\end{array}
$$

REMEMBER
Rewrite the problem and line up the place values if you need to.

6 356 − 187

$$
\begin{array}{ccc}
3 & 5 & 6 \\
- 1 & 8 & 7 \\
\hline
\Box & \Box & \Box
\end{array}
$$

Solve.

I'm going to use place-value models.

7 Alex had 435 coins. He used 182 coins to play games. How many coins does Alex have left? _____

8 Seema had 247 stickers. She gave 139 stickers to her friends last month. How many stickers does Seema have left? _____

DISCUSS **See the Pattern**

Pat wrote some subtraction sentences. He forgot some of the numbers.

Find the missing numbers.

5 − $\Box$ = 4

50 − 10 = $\Box$

500 − $\Box$ = 400

HINT
How does the difference change in each subtraction sentence?

What pattern do you see in these subtraction sentences?

PROBLEM SOLVING

DRIVING TO THE BEACH

READ Zoe drove 214 miles to the beach. Carlos drove 176 miles to the beach. How many more miles did Zoe drive than Carlos?

PLAN
• What is the problem asking you to find?

You need to find how many more _____ Zoe drove than Carlos.

• What do you need to know to solve the problem?

How many miles did Zoe drive? _____

How many miles did Carlos drive? _____

• How can you show the subtraction?

You can line up the numbers by place values.

SOLVE Write the subtraction problem. Line up the numbers by place values.

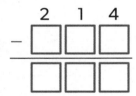

```
    2  1  4
 - □  □  □
 ─────────
   □  □  □
```

CHECK Use addition to check your answer.

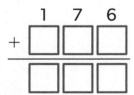

```
    1  7  6
 + □  □  □
 ─────────
   □  □  □
```

Zoe drove _____ more miles than Carlos.

PRACTICE

Use the problem-solving steps to help you.

I can use addition to check my answers.

1 Lake Fishtail is a summer camp for third graders. One summer, 358 girls and 262 boys went to the camp. How many more girls than boys went to Lake Fishtail?

CHECKLIST
☐ READ
☐ PLAN
☐ SOLVE
☐ CHECK

2 A movie theater has 425 seats. One Saturday, 287 people sat in the theater to watch a movie. How many empty seats were there in the theater?

CHECKLIST
☐ READ
☐ PLAN
☐ SOLVE
☐ CHECK

3 Mr. Kim's class planted seeds. The students planted 230 seeds in all. Only 194 of the seeds grew into plants. How many seeds did not grow into plants?

CHECKLIST
☐ READ
☐ PLAN
☐ SOLVE
☐ CHECK

Understanding Multiplication

PLUG IN Adding Equal Groups

An **array** is a group of objects in **rows** and **columns**.

There are 3 columns and 2 rows of stars.

Think of the rows or columns as equal groups.

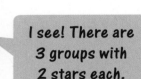

I see! There are 3 groups with 2 stars each.

Add equal groups to find the total.

$2 + 2 + 2 = 6$

When I add the 3 groups, the sum is 6.

Words to Know

array
objects in rows and columns

row
left-to-right group

column
top-to-bottom group

DISCUSS Would you get the same answer if you made 2 groups of 3 stars?

A You can write equal groups in an addition sentence.

DO

1. Count each group. Write the number.

2. Fill in the addition sentence.

3. Add to find the sum.

| 3 | | | |

___3___ + _____ + _____ + _____ = _____

Adding equal groups helps me find the total quickly.

B You can add equal groups without an array.

DO

① Count each group. Write the number.

② Fill in the addition sentence.

③ Add to find the sum.

5   ☐   ☐

_____5_____ + _____ + _____ = _____

C You can make equal groups to match the number sentence.

DO

① Draw triangles to match the addition sentence.

② Add to find the sum.

____2____ + 2 + 2 + 2 = _____

PRACTICE

Fill in the addition sentence. Add to find the sum.

1

4   ☐   ☐   ☐

____4____ + _____ + _____ + _____ = _____

2

_____ + _____ + _____ + _____ + _____ = _____

Draw squares to match the addition sentence. Add to find the sum.

3

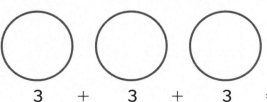

3   +   3   +   3   =   _____

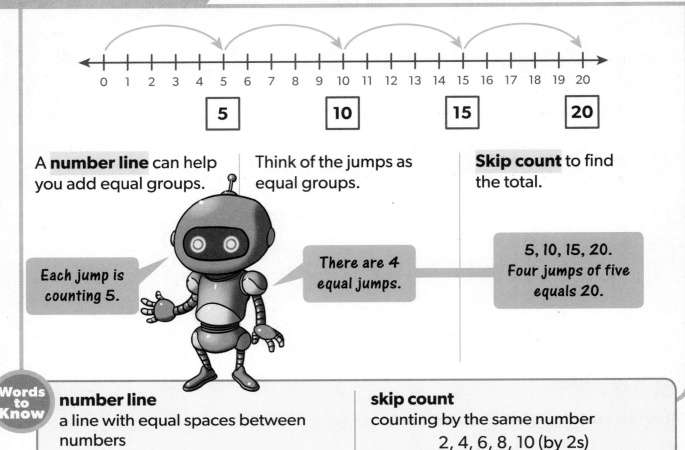

A number line can help you add equal groups.

Think of the jumps as equal groups.

Skip count to find the total.

Each jump is counting 5.

There are 4 equal jumps.

5, 10, 15, 20. Four jumps of five equals 20.

Words to Know

number line
a line with equal spaces between numbers

0 1 2 3 4 5 6 7 8 9 10

skip count
counting by the same number
2, 4, 6, 8, 10 (by 2s)
10, 20, 30, 40, 50 (by 10s)

DISCUSS Why is it important to begin skip counting at zero?

A You can skip count by 2 to find the total.

DO Show 6 jumps of 2.

1 Draw each jump.

2 Write the number below each jump.

3 Find the total.

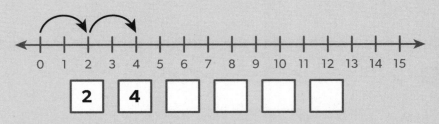

2 4 ☐ ☐ ☐ ☐

The total is _____ .

B You can skip count by 10 to find the total.

Skip counting is another way to add equal groups quickly.

DO   Show 3 jumps of 10.

1 Draw each jump.

2 Find the total.

0 1 2 3 4 5 6 7 8 9 10 11 12 13 14 15 16 17 18 19 20 21 22 23 24 25 26 27 28 29 30

The total is _____ .

DISCUSS   Trent skip counted 2 groups of 5 with this number line. He got 11. What can you tell Trent about his work?

0 1 2 3 4 5 6 7 8 9 10 11 12 13 14 15

PRACTICE

Skip count to find the total.

1 Show 7 jumps of 2.

0 1 2 3 4 5 6 7 8 9 10 11 12 13 14 15

| 2 | | | | | | |

The total is _____ .

2 Show 2 jumps of 10.

0 1 2 3 4 5 6 7 8 9 10 11 12 13 14 15 16 17 18 19 20 21 22 23 24 25 26 27 28 29 30

The total is _____ .

Skip count by 5. Fill in the missing numbers.

3 5, 10, ☐ , 20, ☐ , ☐ , 35, ☐ , ☐ , ☐

Understanding Multiplication

Multiplication is a way to join equal groups.

There are 3 groups of 4.

Write a multiplication sentence using **factors**.

$3 \times 4 = ?$

I see! The factors are 3 and 4.

Find the **product** by finding the total number of objects.

$3 \times 4 = 12$

So, the product is 12.

Words to Know

multiply
combine equal groups

$3 \times 4 = 12$

factors
the numbers you multiply

$\underbrace{3 \times 4}_{\text{factors}} = 12$

product
the answer when numbers are multiplied

$3 \times 4 = \mathbf{12}$
$\uparrow$
product

DISCUSS Would the product be the same if you grouped the objects another way?

LESSON LINK

PLUG IN	POWER UP	GO!

Using an array can help you multiply.

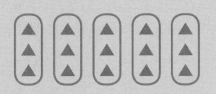

$3 + 3 + 3 + 3 + 3 = 15$
$5 \times 3 = 15$

Skip counting can help you multiply.

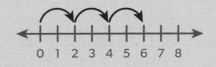

$2 + 2 + 2 = 6$
$3 \times 2 = 6$

I get it! There are many ways to show multiplication.

WORK TOGETHER

Use a Grouping Mat and counters to show multiplication.

- This model shows 5 × 2.
- There are 5 groups with 2 counters in each group.
- There are 10 counters in all. So, the product is 10.

I can use real objects to show joining equal groups.

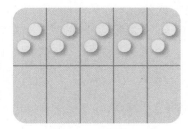

5 × 2 = 10

Grouping Mat and **Counters** can be found on pp. 217 and 219.

A Use a Grouping Mat and some counters to make a model.

DO Model 4 × 5.

1 Show 4 groups with 5 counters in each group.

2 Fill in the multiplication sentence.

3 Find the product.

_____ × _____ = _____

B Use a Grouping Mat and some counters to make a model.

DO Model 7 × 4.

1 Show 7 groups with 4 counters in each group.

2 Fill in the multiplication sentence.

3 Find the product.

_____ × _____ = _____

I can make a model to find the missing factor.

 DISCUSS

Kate wants to find the missing factor of 8 × ☐ = 16.

How can you find the missing factor? What is the missing factor?

PRACTICE

Fill in the multiplication sentence. Find the product.

1

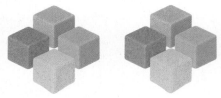  

_____**2**_____ × _____ = _____

HINT
The first factor is the number of equal groups.

2

_____ × _____ = _____

3

★ ★ ★ ★ ★ ★
★ ★ ★ ★ ★ ★
★ ★ ★ ★ ★ ★
★ ★ ★ ★ ★ ★

_____ × _____**4**_____ = _____

REMEMBER
Group the objects first.

4

_____ × _____ = _____

Draw squares in each group to show the multiplication. Find the product.

5 $5 \times 6 =$ _____

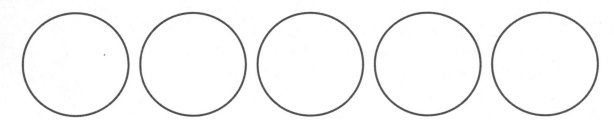

6 $3 \times 9 =$ _____

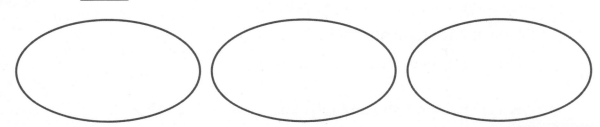

Find the product.

7 Maya has 2 baskets of peaches. There are 8 peaches in each basket. How many peaches are there in all? _____

8 John bought 6 packs of erasers. There are 3 erasers in each pack. How many erasers did John buy in all? _____

> I'm going to make a model by drawing pictures or by using my Grouping Mat.

DISCUSS

See the Pattern

Logan found the products for some multiplication sentences.

Find the missing products.

$4 \times 1 =$ __**4**__ $8 \times 1 =$ __**8**__ $5 \times 1 =$ _____

$9 \times 1 =$ _____ $3 \times 1 =$ _____ $6 \times 1 =$ __**6**__

What pattern do you see in these multiplication sentences?

HINT
What is the same in each multiplication sentence?

71

PROBLEM SOLVING

DOLPHIN FOOD

READ Rita is a dolphin trainer. She will fill buckets with fish. There are 3 buckets. Each bucket will have 8 fish. How many fish will Rita need in all?

PLAN
• What is the problem asking you to find?

You need to find the total number of _____ that Rita needs.

• What do you need to solve the problem?

How many equal groups? _____

How many in each group? _____

• How can you show the multiplication?

You can use an array, skip-count, or make a model.

SOLVE Make a model.

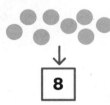 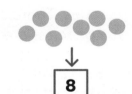

| 8 | | 8 | | 8 |

3 × _____ = _____

CHECK Show the multiplication another way.

Use a number line.

> I get it! If my work is correct, the products will be the same.

Rita will need _____ fish.

PRACTICE

Use the problem-solving steps to help you.

1 Mr. Gordon is buying clay for his class. He will buy 4 bags. Each bag has 5 pieces of clay. How many pieces of clay will Mr. Gordon buy in all?

CHECKLIST
- READ
- PLAN
- SOLVE
- CHECK

2 Jenny made a photo book of a trip. The book has 7 pages. Each page has 2 photos. What is the total number of photos in Jenny's photo book?

CHECKLIST
- READ
- PLAN
- SOLVE
- CHECK

3 Dalton works at a phone store. He worked 5 days this week. He sold 10 phones each day. How many phones did Dalton sell in all?

CHECKLIST
- READ
- PLAN
- SOLVE
- CHECK

8 Multiplication Facts

PLUG IN Repeated Addition

The array shows 5 groups of 3.

Write an addition sentence to find the total.

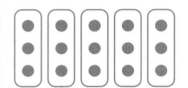

$3 + 3 + 3 + 3 + 3 = \boxed{}$

Add to find the total.

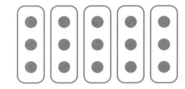

$3 + 3 + 3 + 3 + 3 = 15$

I remember! An array is a group of objects in rows and columns.

I need to add 3 five times because there are 5 groups of 3.

So 5 groups of 3 is equal to 15.

DISCUSS How does an array help you quickly find the total number of objects?

A You can write an addition sentence to show repeated addition.

DO

❶ Count each group. Write the number.

❷ Fill in the addition sentence.

❸ Add to find the total.

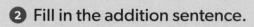

$4 \ + \ \underline{} \ + \ \underline{} \ + \ \underline{} \ = \ \underline{}$

B You also can make an array to match an addition sentence.

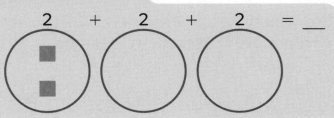

$$2 \ + \ 2 \ + \ 2 \ = \ \underline{}$$

DO

1 Draw squares to match the addition sentence.

2 Add to find the total.

PRACTICE

Fill in the addition sentence. Add to find the total.

I see! There are 2 circles in each group.

1
● ● ● ● ●
● ● ● ● ●
↓ ↓ ↓ ↓ ↓
<u>2</u> + ___ + ___ + ___ + ___ = ___

2
● ●
● ●
● ●
● ●
● ●
↓ ↓
___ + ___ = ___

3
● ● ●
● ● ●
● ● ●
↓ ↓ ↓
___ + ___ + ___ = ___

Draw triangles to match the addition sentence. Add to find the total.

4   4   +   4   = __

5   1   +   1   +   1   +   1   +   1   = __

Representing Multiplication

You can show 2 × 7 as 2 groups of 7 objects.

Put 7 squares in each group.

Count the total number of squares.

7 + 7 = 14

2 × 7 = 14

I see! The ovals show the 2 groups.

Now I have 2 groups of 7 squares.

There are 14 squares in all, so 2 × 7 = 14.

DISCUSS Would the product be the same if you made 7 groups of 2 stars?

A You can use equal groups to show multiplication.

 Show 4 × 2 as 4 groups of 2.

❶ The ovals show the 4 groups.

❷ Draw 2 triangles in each group.

❸ Count all the triangles.

❹ Fill in the number sentences.

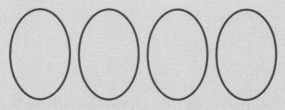

———— + ———— + ———— + ———— = ————

———— × ———— = ————

B You can use an array to show multiplication.

DO Show 3 × 2 as columns and rows.

❶ The rectangles show 3 columns.

❷ Draw 2 triangles in each column.

❸ How many in each column?

❹ Fill in the number sentences.

———— + ———— + ———— = ————

———— × ———— = ————

C You also can use a number line to show multiplication.

DO Show 3 × 6 as 3 jumps of 6.

1 A jump of 6 is shown.

2 Draw 2 more jumps of 6.

3 Write the total.

4 Fill in the number sentence.

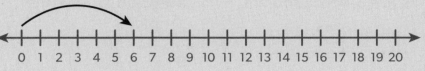

The total is _____

_____ × _____ = _____

DISCUSS Juanita made equal groups to show 4 × 7. She says that 4 × 7 = 24.

Is her work correct?

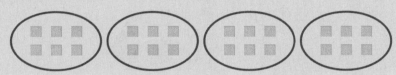

PRACTICE

Draw squares in equal groups to show the multiplication. Write the total.

1 3 × 7

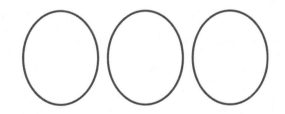

3 × 7 = _____

Draw triangles in an array to show the multiplication. Write the total.

2 5 × 2

5 × 2 = _____

Draw jumps on a number line to show the multiplication. Write the total.

3 4 × 5

4 × 5 = _____

READY TO GO Multiplication Facts

Make a model to help solve a word problem.

There are 3 rows of chairs. Each row has 8 chairs. How many chairs in all are there?

I see 3 rows of 8 chairs in the array!

You can use **repeated addition** to solve the problem.

$8 + 8 + 8 = \boxed{}$

$8 + 8 + 8 = 24$

I can add 8 3 times.

You can write an **equation** to represent the word problem and solve.

$3 \times 8 = \boxed{}$

3 times 8 equals 24.

 Words to Know

repeated addition adding the same number more than once

equation a number sentence with an = to show equal amounts

DISCUSS When solving a word problem, how do you know whether to add or multiply?

LESSON LINK

PLUG IN	POWER UP	GO!

Repeated addition can help you with your multiplication facts.

$4 + 4 + 4 = 12$

$3 \times 4 = 12$

Models also can help you with your multiplication facts.

• • • •
• • • •

$4 \times 2 = 8$

OK! So knowing about repeated addition and modeling can help me solve multiplication word problems.

WORK TOGETHER

Use repeated addition to solve the word problem.

- Read the problem to find what it is asking.
- Write a multiplication equation to show your answer.

Amanda has 7 cups. She put 5 cherries in each cup. How many cherries did she use?

$5 + 5 + 5 + 5 + 5 + 5 + 5 = 35$

$7 \times 5 = 35$

Amanda used 35 cherries.

A Draw a model to show your work. Write an equation and solve.

 Mrs. Garcia made 8 stacks of books. She put 4 books in each stack. How many books did she stack in all?

1. Draw a model.
2. Write a multiplication equation.
3. Solve the problem.

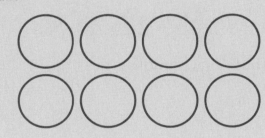

_____ × _____ = _____

Mrs. Garcia stacked _____ books.

B Use repeated addition to solve. Write a multiplication equation.

There are 6 happy faces on each page. There are 4 pages. How many happy faces are there in all?

1. Use repeated addition to solve. _____ + _____ + _____ + _____ = _____
2. Write a multiplication equation. _____ × _____ = _____
3. Solve the problem.   There are _____ happy faces.

DISCUSS Jonathan wants to show 9×5 in a different way. How can you change one of the factors to show it a different way? Would you get the same answer?

PRACTICE

Use repeated addition or models to show your work.

1 John read 9 pages of his favorite book every night. He read for 5 nights. How many pages did he read in all?

___9___ + _____ + _____ + _____ + _____ = _____

_____ × _____ = _____

John read _____ pages.

2 Sue bought 3 aquariums. She placed 6 goldfish in each aquarium. How many goldfish does she have?

_____ × _____ = _____

Sue has _____ goldfish.

3 There are 6 pencils in each box. There are 7 boxes. How many pencils are there?

_____ × _____ = _____

There are _____ pencils.

4 There are 4 vases with 7 long-stemmed roses in each vase. How many long-stemmed roses are there?

_____ + _____ + _____ + _____ = _____

_____ × _____ = _____

There are _____ long-stemmed roses.

Solve.

5 Nellie has 3 bags with 8 marbles in each bag. How many marbles does Nellie have in all?

_____

6 Rudy has 9 sheets of stickers. There are 7 stickers on each sheet. How many stickers does Rudy have in all?

_____

See the Pattern

Pam found the products for some multiplication sentences. Find the missing products.

$1 \times 10 = 10$ 3×10 _____ 5×10 _____

2×10 _____ $4 \times 10 = 40$ $6 \times 10 = 60$

What pattern do you see in these multiplication sentences?

HINT
What happens when you multiply a number by 10?

PROBLEM SOLVING

EGG CARTONS

READ Nathan has an egg carton that holds 5 rows of 11 eggs each. How many eggs can the carton hold?

PLAN
- What are you asked to find?

    You need to find the total number of _____ that a carton can hold.

- What do you know?

    Each carton holds _____ rows of eggs.

    There are _____ eggs in each row.

- What property can help you find the product?

    You can use the distributive property to find the product.

SOLVE Use the distributive property to multiply 5×11.

$5 \times 11 = 5 \times (6 + \underline{\hspace{1cm}})$

$\qquad = (5 \times \underline{\hspace{1cm}}) + (5 \times \underline{\hspace{1cm}})$

$\qquad = \underline{\hspace{1cm}} + \underline{\hspace{1cm}}$

$\qquad = \underline{\hspace{1cm}}$

CHECK Break apart the factor a different way.

$5 \times 11 = 5 \times (\underline{\hspace{1cm}} + 1)$

$\qquad = (5 \times \underline{\hspace{1cm}}) + (5 \times \underline{\hspace{1cm}})$

$\qquad = \underline{\hspace{1cm}} + \underline{\hspace{1cm}}$

$\qquad = \underline{\hspace{1cm}}$

The carton can hold _____ eggs.

PRACTICE

Use the problem-solving steps to help you.

1 Mrs. Olsen teaches 2 classes. She has 13 students in each class. How many students does Mrs. Olsen teach in all?

CHECKLIST
- [ ] READ
- [ ] PLAN
- [ ] SOLVE
- [ ] CHECK

2 Carlos jogged 3 miles each day. He jogged for 11 days. How many miles did Carlos jog in all?

CHECKLIST
- [ ] READ
- [ ] PLAN
- [ ] SOLVE
- [ ] CHECK

3 Bethany baked 4 batches of cookies. There were 12 cookies in each batch. What was the total number of cookies Bethany baked?

CHECKLIST
- [ ] READ
- [ ] PLAN
- [ ] SOLVE
- [ ] CHECK

Understanding Division

Skip Counting Backward

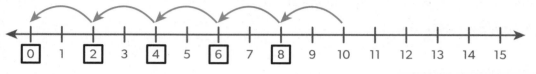

A number line can help you subtract equal groups.

Think of each jump as an equal group.

Skip count backward to find the total number of groups.

8, 6, 4, 2, 0

Each jump is counting back 2.

There are 5 equal jumps.

I counted back by 2 five times, so there are 5 groups of 2 in 10.

Words to Know

skip count backward
to count backward by the same number

10, 8, 6, 4, 2, 0 (by 2s)

50, 40, 30, 20, 10, 0 (by 10s)

 DISCUSS Why should you always end at 0 when skip counting backward to find the total number of groups?

A You can skip count backward to find the total number of groups.

DO Skip count backward by 5 starting at 15.

❶ Draw each jump.

❷ Count the jumps.

❸ Write the total number of groups.

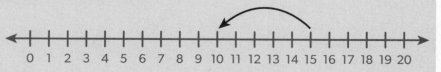

There are _____ groups of 5 in 15.

B You can skip count backward to find the total number of groups.

DO Skip count backward by 3 starting at 18.

1 Draw each jump.

2 Count the jumps.

3 Write the total number of groups.

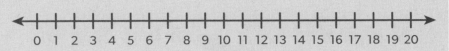

There are _____ groups of 3 in 18.

DISCUSS Quincy started at 12 and skip counted backward by 4 to find the total number of groups using this number line.

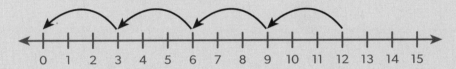

What can you tell Quincy about his work?

PRACTICE

Skip count backward to find the total number of groups.

1 Start at 16. Skip count backward by 4.

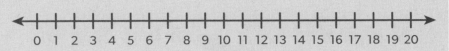

There are _____ groups of 4 in 16.

2 Start at 14. Skip count backward by 2.

There are _____ groups of 2 in 14.

3 90, 80, ☐, ☐, 50, ☐, 30, ☐, 10, ☐

There are _____ groups of _____ in 90.

Modeling Division

Models can be used to show division.

Divide the apples into groups of 2.

Make groups of 2 until no apples are left. Count the number of groups.

Look! There are 6 apples.

Put 2 apples in each group.

Got it! There are 3 groups of 2 in 6.

DISCUSS What would happen if you put the apples into groups of 3?

A You can use a model to show a division fact.

DO Divide 8 ÷ 4.

❶ Draw to show the total number.

❷ Circle the dots to make groups of 4.

❸ Count the groups. Write the number.

❹ Fill in the division sentence.

8 ÷ 4

There are _____ groups of 4 in 8.

8 ÷ 4 = _____

B You can write a division fact to match a model.

DO

❶ Count the total number of objects.

❷ Count the number in each group.

❸ Count the number of groups.

❹ Fill in the division sentence.

There are _____ groups of 6 in 18.

18 ÷ _____ = _____

Julia used a model to show a division fact.

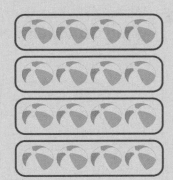

What division fact does Julia's model show?

PRACTICE

Make equal groups. Complete the division sentences.

1 Show groups of 6.

★ ★ ★ ★ ★ ★
★ ★ ★ ★ ★ ★
★ ★ ★ ★ ★ ★
★ ★ ★ ★ ★ ★

There are _____ groups of 6 in 30.

$30 \div 6 =$ _____

2 Show groups of 4.

There are _____ groups of 4 in 24.

$24 \div 4 =$ _____

Write a division fact to match each model.

3

$20 \div$ _____ = _____

4

_____ $\div$ _____ = _____

Division is a way to put objects into equal groups.

I see! 12 objects are being divided into 4 equal groups.

Write a division sentence using a **dividend** and **divisor**.

$12 \div 4 = \square$

The dividend is 12 and the divisor is 4.

Find the **quotient** by counting the number of objects in one group.

$12 \div 4 = 3$

Got it! When 12 is divided into 4 equal groups, 3 is the quotient.

Words to Know

dividend
the number to be divided

divisor
a number that divides another number

quotient
the answer to a division problem

DISCUSS How would a model for $12 \div 3 = 4$ be similar to the model for $12 \div 4 = 3$? How would it be different?

LESSON LINK

PLUG IN ▸ **POWER UP** ▸ **GO!**

Skip counting backward can help you find the total number of groups.

0 1 2 3 4 5 6 7 8 9 10

Using models can help you divide.

$12 \div 3 = 4$

Now I know! I can use different ways to show division facts!

I can use a Grouping Mat to divide real objects into equal groups.

WORK TOGETHER

Use a Grouping Mat and counters to show division.

• This model shows 15 ÷ 5.

• There are 15 counters in all.

• There are 5 equal groups.

• There 3 counters in each group. So the quotient is 3.

$$15 \div 5 = 3$$

Grouping Mat and **Counters** can be found on p. 221 and 223.

A Use a Grouping Mat and some counters to make a model.

DO Model 24 ÷ 6.

❶ Count out 24 objects.

❷ Divide them into 6 equal groups.

❸ Count the number in each group.

❹ Fill in the division sentence.

❺ Find the quotient.

_____ ÷ _____ = _____

B Use a Grouping Mat and objects to find the missing divisor.

DO Model 20 ÷ ☐ = 4.

❶ Count out 20 objects.

❷ Put 4 objects at a time in each group until none are left.

❸ Count the number of groups.

❹ Fill in the divisor.

20 ÷ _____ = 4

I can use a model to work backward and find the missing dividend.

DISCUSS How can Tim find the missing dividend of ☐ ÷ 4 = 8?

What is the missing dividend?

PRACTICE

Complete each division sentence. Use the number in each group as the divisor.

1

$36 \div 9 = $ _____

> **HINT**
> The quotient is the number of groups.

2

$21 \div $ _____ $ = $ _____

> **REMEMBER**
> The divisor is the number in each group.

3

_____ $\div$ _____ $= 8$

4

_____ $\div$ _____ $= 7$

Draw circles in each group to show the division. Find the dividend.

5 _____ $\div 4 = 12$

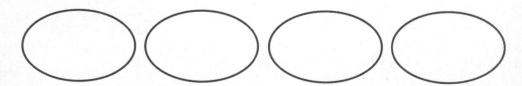

> **HINT**
> Draw one circle at a time in each group until you have 12 in each group.

6 _____ ÷ 6 = 6

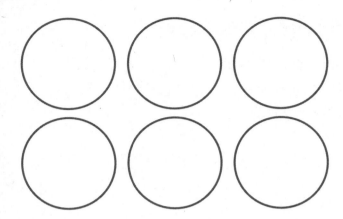

Find the quotients.

7 Marta has 18 stamps. She wants to give an equal number of stamps to each of 3 friends. How many stamps can she give each friend?   _____

8 Mr. Wallace has 40 apples. He needs to put an equal number of apples in 8 baskets. How many apples can he put in each basket?   _____

I'm going to draw a picture to help me divide these numbers into equal groups.

Find the Mistake

Brian made a mistake while drawing a picture to show the division fact 24 ÷ 8 = 3.

Find the mistake.

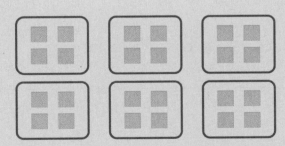

What mistake did Brian make?

Why is it important to correctly model each part of a division fact?

PROBLEM SOLVING

MAKING LEMONADE

READ

India has 36 lemons. She needs 4 lemons to make a pitcher of lemonade. How many pitchers of lemonade can she make using all 36 lemons?

PLAN

• Think about what you know.

There are a total of _____ lemons.

There are _____ lemons in each group.

• Think about what you need to find out.

You need to find the number of _____ India can make.

• How can you show the division?

You can use a Grouping Mat, draw a picture, or skip count backward.

SOLVE

Draw a picture.

$36 \div$ _____ $=$ _____

CHECK

Skip count backward to check your answer.

$36 \div$ _____ $=$ _____

India can make _____ pitchers of lemonade.

PRACTICE

Use the problem-solving steps to find each answer.

1 Sawyer has 20 blocks. He wants to build towers that are each 5 blocks tall. How many towers can he build?

CHECKLIST
- [ ] READ
- [ ] PLAN
- [ ] SOLVE
- [ ] CHECK

2 7 students share equally a snack of 35 grapes. How many grapes does each student get?

CHECKLIST
- [ ] READ
- [ ] PLAN
- [ ] SOLVE
- [ ] CHECK

3 Mrs. Newton has 18 tests to grade. She has 3 hours to spend grading tests. How many tests does she need to grade each hour?

CHECKLIST
- [ ] READ
- [ ] PLAN
- [ ] SOLVE
- [ ] CHECK

Division Facts

PLUG IN Understanding Multiplication

When you multiply two **factors**, you are adding equal groups.

$$5 \times 7$$
$$7 + 7 + 7 + 7 + 7$$

The **product** is the total number in all of the groups.

$$5 \times 7 = 35$$
$$7 + 7 + 7 + 7 + 7 = 35$$

A model can show multiplication.

$$5 \times 7$$

$$5 \times 7 = 35$$

The two factors are 5 and 7.

The sum $7 + 7 + 7 + 7 + 7$ is 35. So the product 5×7 is 35.

I see! $5 \times 7 = 35$ shows the total number of objects in 5 groups of 7.

Words to Know

factors
the numbers you multiply

product
the answer when numbers are multiplied

DISCUSS What does the multiplication sentence $8 \times 3 = 24$ represent?

A You can use models to find a missing factor in a multiplication sentence.

DO

$$2 \times \boxed{} = 16$$

❶ Draw 16 circles to show the product.

❷ Make 2 equal groups to show the given factor.

❸ Count how many in each group.

❹ Write the multiplication sentence.

The missing factor is ___**8**___.

$$2 \times \underline{} = 16$$

B Models can help you find a missing factor.

DO $\boxed{} \times 4 = 24$

❶ Draw 24 triangles to show the product.

❷ Make equal groups of 4 to show the given factor.

❸ Count how many groups.

❹ Write the multiplication sentence.

The missing factor is _____.

_____ $\times 4 = 24$

PRACTICE

Write multiplication sentences to match the models.

1

_____

2

_____

Find the missing factors. Draw models to help you.

3 $6 \times \boxed{} = 12$

4 $\boxed{} \times 3 = 27$

Understanding Division

When you **divide** a whole number, you make equal groups.

I need to equally divide 18 into groups of 3.

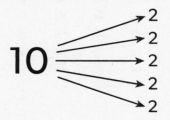

An array can show the **quotient** as the number in each group.

18 ÷ 3 = 6

There are 6 in each of 3 groups, so the quotient is 6.

An array can also show the quotient as the number of groups.

18 ÷ 3 = 6

There are 6 equal groups of 3. So the quotient is still 6!

Words to Know

divide
to split into equal parts or groups

10 → 2
→ 2
→ 2
→ 2
→ 2

quotient
the answer to a division equation

45 ÷ 9 = 5

↑
quotient

DISCUSS If 18 ÷ 6 = 3, what is the quotient of 18 ÷ 3? How do you know?

A You can use models to find the missing divisor in a division sentence.

DO 15 ÷ ☐ = 3

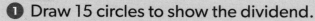

1. Draw 15 circles to show the dividend.
2. Make equal groups of 3.
3. Count how many groups.
4. Write the division sentence.

The divisor is __5__ .

15 ÷ ☐ = 3

B You can use models to find the missing dividend in a division sentence.

1 Draw 7 triangles to show the quotient.

2 Since the divisor is 3, make 2 more equal groups of 7.

3 Count the total number of triangles.

4 Write the division sentence.

The dividend is _____.

_____ ÷ 3 = 7

DISCUSS Kristy wants to find the missing dividend in ☐ ÷ 4 = 3. How can she find the dividend? What is the dividend?

PRACTICE

Write division sentences to match the models. Use the numbers of groups for the divisors.

1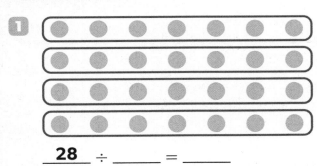

____28____ ÷ _____ = _____

2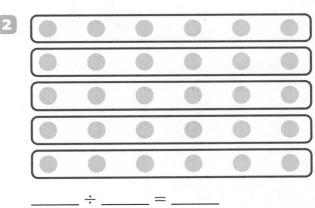

_____ ÷ _____ = _____

Find the missing divisor. Draw a model to help you.

3 $45 \div \boxed{} = 5$

Find the missing dividend. Draw a model to help you.

4 $\boxed{} \div 8 = 6$

You can write an equation to represent a word problem.

Samuel placed 25 oranges equally in 5 baskets. How many oranges are in each basket?

$25 \div 5 = \boxed{}$

You can use repeated subtraction to find the quotient.

Start with 25 and subtract 5 each time until you get to 0.

$25 - 5 = 20$
$20 - 5 = 15$
$15 - 5 = 10$
$10 - 5 = 5$
$5 - 5 = 0$

I see! I can subtract 5 five times until I get to 0.

You can use a model to solve a division equation.

$25 \div 5 = \boxed{}$

$25 \div 5 = 5$

I get it! 25 divided by 5 equals 5.

DISCUSS Explain how you can use the numbers 2, 3, and 6 to write four different equations. Hint: two of the equations will use multiplication and two will use division.

LESSON LINK

PLUG IN	POWER UP	GO!
Multiplying is putting together equal groups.	**Dividing is breaking apart into equal groups.**	I can use division and multiplication to help me solve word problems.
$6 \times 7 = 42$	$42 \div 7 = 6$	
6 groups of 7 equals 42	42 broken into 7 equal groups equals 6	

WORK TOGETHER

Use Grouping Mats to show division.

• Write an equation to represent the problem.

• The model shows 48 counters in 8 equal groups.

• There are 6 counters in each group.

• $48 \div 8 = 6$. The quotient is 6. There are 6 buttons in each group.

Rose has 48 buttons. She put them in 8 equal groups. How many buttons are in each group?

$48 \div 8 = \boxed{}$

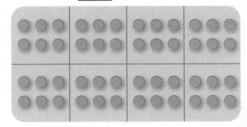

Grouping Mat and **Counters** can be found on p. 225 and 227.

A Use a Grouping Mat and counters to show division.

 $63 \div 7 = \boxed{}$

❶ Write an equation to represent the problem.

❷ Count 63 objects. Place them into 7 equal groups.

❸ Count the number in each group.

❹ Write the quotient.

63 computers were divided equally among 7 classrooms. How many computers did each classroom get?

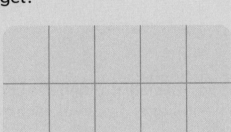

$63 \div 7 =$ _____

Each classroom got _____ computers.

I can multiply to check the answer to a division problem!

DISCUSS Tara wants to make sure her answer is correct in the following division problem: $36 \div 6 = 6$. How can Tara check her answer? Is the answer correct?

PRACTICE

Write a division equation to represent each division problem and solve.
Use multiplication to check each quotient.

1 There are 22 students in gym class. They were divided equally
into 2 teams. How many students are on each team?

22 ÷ **2** = _____

_____ students

11 × **2** = _____

HINT
The divisor and
quotient are the
two factors in
a multiplication
fact.

2 Mr. Rodriguez had 42 erasers. He gave an equal number to each of 7 students.
How many erasers did he give to each student?

_____ ÷ _____ = _____

_____ erasers

_____ × _____ = _____

3 Edward has 40 math problems to complete in 8 days. He wants to complete
an equal number of problems each day. How many does he need to complete
each day?

_____ ÷ _____ = _____

_____ math problems

_____ × _____ = _____

4 There are 50 bottles of orange juice. 10 people each get an equal number
of bottles. How many bottles of juice does each person get?

_____ ÷ _____ = _____

_____ bottles

_____ × _____ = _____

Find each quotient.

Check your answer with a multiplication fact using **9** as one of the factors and **45** as the product.

5 Huan has 45 stamps. He places 9 stamps on each page of a book. How many pages have stamps?

_____

6 Suzanne bought 32 boxes of raisins. There were 8 boxes in a pack. How many packs of raisins did Suzanne buy?

_____

7 Tyrone has 35 pencils. He gives an equal number of pencils to each of 7 friends. How many pencils does he give to each friend?

_____

8 Lily used 54 beads to make 6 necklaces. All the necklaces had the same number of beads. How many beads were there in each necklace?

_____

Not Enough Information

Read the word problem. Decide what information is missing.

Carrie has 72 oranges and needs to make 8 glasses of orange juice. Does she have enough oranges?

What information do you need in order to solve the problem?

PROBLEM SOLVING

ARCADE GAMES

READ Braden has 56 tokens. Each arcade game takes 8 tokens. How many games can Braden play in all?

PLAN • Figure out what you know.

Braden has _____ tokens.

Each game takes _____ tokens.

• Figure out what you need to find.

I need to find the number of _____ Braden can play.

• What number do you need to divide? Into how many groups will you divide that number?

I need to divide _____ by _____.

SOLVE Write the division problem. Draw a model to show the division of 56 by 8.

$56 \div 8 = \boxed{}$

$56 \div 8 = $ _____

CHECK Use multiplication to check your answer.

$56 \div 8 = 7$

$7 \times 8 = 56$

Braden can play _____ games.

PRACTICE

Use the problem-solving steps to help you.

1 Phillip picked 81 strawberries and divided them equally into 9 baskets. How many strawberries did Phillip place in each basket?

CHECKLIST
- [ ] READ
- [ ] PLAN
- [ ] SOLVE
- [ ] CHECK

2 Molly collected an equal number of glass bottles each day. She collected a total of 72 bottles. She spent 8 days collecting them. How many bottles did Molly collect each day?

CHECKLIST
- [ ] READ
- [ ] PLAN
- [ ] SOLVE
- [ ] CHECK

3 Mr. Ramirez drives to work 5 days a week. In one week, he drives a total of 35 miles. How many miles does he drive to and from work each day?

CHECKLIST
- [ ] READ
- [ ] PLAN
- [ ] SOLVE
- [ ] CHECK

Solving Two-Step Word Problems

PLUG IN Rounding Whole Numbers

Use **place value** to round. To **round** to the nearest 10, look at the digit in the ones place. If it is 5 or greater, round up.

348

Hundreds	Tens	Ones
3	4	8

To the nearest ten, 348 rounds to 350.

You can use a number line to round. To round to the nearest 100, find the two hundreds the number is between. Round to the closer hundred.

348

300 310 320 330 340 350 360 370 380 390 400

To the nearest hundred, 348 rounds to 300.

> When I use place value to round to the nearest 10, I compare the digit in the ones place to 5.

> When I use a number line to round to the nearest 100, I find which hundred the number is closer to.

Words to Know

place value
the value of a digit based on its position in a number

round
to find the value closest to a number

DISCUSS How does a number line help you to round?

A You can use a number line to round to the nearest 100.

DO Round 338 to the nearest 100.

❶ Find the number 338.

❷ Compare 338 to 300 and 400.

338

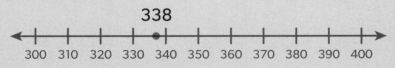
300 310 320 330 340 350 360 370 380 390 400

❸ Write the rounded number.

338 is closer to __300__.

To the nearest hundred, 338 rounds to _____.

Look at the digit to the right of the place you are rounding to.

B You can use place value to round to the nearest 100.

DO Round 618 to the nearest 100.

❶ Look at the tens digit. Compare the digit to 5.

❷ Round down. Replace the tens digit and ones digit with 0.

❸ Write the rounded number.

618

Hundreds	Tens	Ones
6	1	8

The digit in the tens place is __1__.

1 is _____ than 5.

To the nearest hundred, 618 rounds to _____.

C You can use place value to round to the nearest 10.

DO Round 618 to the nearest 10.

❶ Look at the ones digit. Compare the digit to 5.

❷ Round up. Add 1 to the tens digit. Replace the ones digit with 0.

❸ Write the rounded number.

618

Hundreds	Tens	Ones
6	1	8

The digit in the ones place is _____.

8 is _____ than 5.

To the nearest ten, 618 rounds to _____.

PRACTICE

Round to the nearest 10.

1

Hundreds	Tens	Ones
7	8	4

784 rounds to _____.

Round to the nearest 100.

2

Hundreds	Tens	Ones
1	4	7

147 rounds to _____.

Round to the nearest 100.

3

656

600 610 620 630 640 650 660 670 680 690 700

656 rounds to _____.

Adding, Subtracting, Multiplying, and Dividing

Addition and subtraction are **inverse operations**.

$$
\begin{array}{r} 24 \\ +35 \\ \hline 59 \end{array}
\qquad
\begin{array}{r} 59 \\ -35 \\ \hline 24 \end{array}
$$

Multiplication and division are also inverse operations.

$$2 \times 3 = 6$$
$$6 \div 3 = 2$$

> I see! Inverse operations undo each other.

Use **fact families** to add and subtract.

$$9 + 6 = 15 \qquad 15 - 6 = 9$$
$$6 + 9 = 15 \qquad 15 - 9 = 6$$

Use fact families to multiply and divide.

$$3 \times 4 = 12 \qquad 12 \div 4 = 3$$
$$4 \times 3 = 12 \qquad 12 \div 3 = 4$$

> Fact families can help you remember the facts.

Words to Know

inverse operations
operations that undo each other

fact family
a set of related facts that use the same numbers

DISCUSS Do all fact families have 4 related facts? Explain and give an example.

A You can use subtraction to check addition problems.

 DO Add 263 + 224.

❶ Add the ones, tens, and hundreds.

❷ Check your answer. Subtract 224 from the sum.

❸ Find the difference. Compare the difference to 263. Both should be the same.

	Hundreds	Tens	Ones
+	2	6	3
	2	2	4
			7

Check.

	Hundreds	Tens	Ones
	☐	☐	☐
−	2	2	4
	☐	☐	☐

B You can use inverse operations to write fact families.

 Write a fact family for the array.

1 Count the number of rows and columns.

2 Count the total number of triangles.

3 Write the related multiplication facts.

4 Write the related division facts.

There are ___**3**___ rows and _____ columns.

There are _____ triangles.

_____ × _____ = _____   _____ ÷ _____ = _____

_____ × _____ = _____   _____ ÷ _____ = _____

DISCUSS If you know that $6 \times 5 = 30$, what other facts do you know? How can fact families help you write the facts?

PRACTICE

Add. Then subtract to check your sum.

1 $412 + 367$

	Hundreds	Tens	Ones
	4	1	2
+	3	6	7
			9

Check your sum.

	Hundreds	Tens	Ones
	☐	☐	☐
−	3	6	7
	☐	☐	☐

Write the multiplication and division fact family.

2

_____ × _____ = _____   _____ ÷ _____ = _____

_____ × _____ = _____   _____ ÷ _____ = _____

READY TO GO   Solving Two-Step Word Problems

There are 29 students in Al's class. There are 22 students in Meg's class. How many students are in the two classes in all?

Look for key words or phrases to tell which operations to use.

Add: in all, all together
Subtract: how many more, how many left
Multiply: in all, all together (for equal groups)
Divide: how many groups

> I need to add to find how many students in all.

Write **equations** to solve word problems. Use a letter to stand for a number.

$$29 + 22 = b$$
$$29 + 22 = 51$$
$$b = 51$$

Use rounding to **estimate** when adding or subtracting.

$$
\begin{array}{rcr}
29 & \rightarrow & 30 \\
+22 & \rightarrow & +20 \\
\hline
 & & 50
\end{array}
$$

> I can estimate to check if my answer is reasonable.

Words to Know

equation	**estimate**
a sentence that uses = to show equal amounts	to round numbers to check if an answer is reasonable

DISCUSS When solving a word problem, how do you know when to add or multiply?

LESSON LINK

PLUG IN	POWER UP	GO!

Numbers can be rounded to the nearest ten or hundred.

To the nearest ten, 431 rounds to 430.

To the nearest hundred, 431 rounds to 400.

Knowing fact families helps you quickly add, subtract, multiply, and divide.

$2 + 4 = 6$	$2 \times 4 = 8$
$4 + 2 = 6$	$4 \times 2 = 8$
$6 - 2 = 4$	$8 \div 2 = 4$
$6 - 4 = 2$	$8 \div 4 = 2$

> I get it! I can round numbers to check if my solution to a word problem makes sense.

WORK TOGETHER

James bought 3 used books for $6 each. He paid with a $20 bill.
How much change should James get back?

I can use a letter to stand for the number I want to find.

• Write what you know

• Write equations

  Step 1. Multiply to find the total cost of the books.

  Step 2. Subtract to find the amount of change.

• Solve each equation.

• Write the answers.

James bought 3 books for $6 each. He used a $20 bill to pay.

Let t = the total cost of the books
$3 \times \$6 = t$
$3 \times \$6 = \$18$, so $t = \$18$.

Let c = James's money
$\$20 - \$18 = c$
$\$20 - \$18 = \$2$, so $c = \$2$.

The total cost of the books is $18.
James should get back $2.

A You can write equations to solve a word problem.

Alanis baked 38 cookies. She kept 6 cookies for her family. She gave an equal number of cookies to 8 friends. How many cookies did each friend receive?

❶ Write an equation to find the total number of cookies given to friends.

❷ Subtract to solve the equation.

$38 - 6 = c$

Let c = the total number of cookies given to friends

$38 - 6 =$ _____, so $c =$ _____.

Alanis gave _____ cookies to her friends.

❸ Use the answer from Step 2. Write an equation to find the number of cookies each friend received.

❹ Divide to solve the equation.

$32 \div 8 = f$

Let f = the number of cookies each friend received

$32 \div 8 =$ _____, so $f =$ _____.

Each friend received _____ cookies.

DISCUSS   How can you use estimation to determine if the answer is reasonable?

PRACTICE

Write equations. Then solve.

1 A bag has 75 balloons. There are 30 blue balloons and 20 white balloons. The rest are red. How many red balloons are there?

Let b = the number of blue balloons and white balloons

$30 + 20 = b$

HINT
First, find how many blue and white balloons are in the bag.

_____ red balloons

2 Mark has 5 shelves. Each shelf has 2 model cars and 4 model planes. How many models are on his shelves in all?

_____ models in all

3 Ava picked 16 oranges and 20 apples. She will give 9 friends the same number of pieces of fruit. How many pieces of fruit will each friend get?

REMEMBER
Round to make sure your answer is reasonable.

_____ pieces of fruit

Write equations to solve. Round the numbers and estimate to check your answer.

4 Roger bought a pair of pants for $18 and a shirt for $34. If he had $78, how much money does he have left?

5 Sue bought 4 packs of baseball cards. Each pack contains 8 cards. She already had 87 cards. How many cards does Sue have now?

Solve.

6 Mrs. Wong bought 3 books for $7 each. She paid for the books with $30. How much change did she receive? _____

> I can write an equation for each part of the problem.

7 Claire bought 2 adult movie tickets and 3 student tickets. Each adult ticket cost $11 and each student ticket cost $9. How much did Claire spend on the tickets? _____

DISCUSS

Check the Reasoning

Avery has 40 minutes to take a test. The first problem took her 10 minutes. There are 5 other problems she must solve. She wants to find how much time she has left to finish each of the other 5 problems. She wrote her reasoning.

I add $40 + 10 = 50$ and then I divide $50 \div 5 = 10$. I have 10 minutes to solve each of the other 5 problems.

Is Avery correct? Explain why or why not?

HINT
Look for key words and phrases. Subtract when you want to find out how many are left.

PROBLEM SOLVING

FIELD TRIP

READ
Some students from 4 different classes are going on a field trip. There are 3 boys and 3 girls from each class who are going. How many students are going in all?

PLAN
• What is the problem asking you to find?

You need to find the number of students going on the trip.

• What do you need to know to solve the problem?

There are _____ boys and _____ girls from each class going.

There are students from _____ different classes going.

• How can you find the number of students?

You can write equations and solve.

SOLVE
Write two equations.

Let s = the number of students from each class
$s = 3 + 3$
$3 + 3 =$ _____, so $s =$ _____

Let t = the total number of students
$t = 6 \times 4$
$6 \times 4 =$ _____, so $t =$ _____

_____ students are going on the trip.

CHECK
Draw a picture.

$6 + 6 + 6 + 6 =$ _____

There are _____ students going on the trip.

PRACTICE

Write equations and use the problem-solving steps to help you. Estimate to check your answer.

1 Patti bought 4 scarves for $6 each. She also bought a jacket for $57. How much money did Patti spend in all?

Let s = the amount of money spent on scarves

Let m = the amount of money Patti spent in all

CHECKLIST
- [ ] READ
- [ ] PLAN
- [ ] SOLVE
- [ ] CHECK

$_____ spent in all

2 A play is 75 minutes long. The first act is 45 minutes long. There are 3 scenes in the second act. If each scene in the second act takes the same number of minutes, how many minutes will each scene last?

Let m = the number of minutes in the second act

Let s = the number of minutes each scene will last

CHECKLIST
- [ ] READ
- [ ] PLAN
- [ ] SOLVE
- [ ] CHECK

_____ minutes

3 Mr. Richards has 58 DVDs in his collection. He has 19 drama DVDs and 26 comedy DVDs. The rest of the DVDs are concerts. How many concert DVDs does Mr. Richards have?

Let d = the total number of drama and comedy DVDs

Let c = the number of concert DVDs

CHECKLIST
- [ ] READ
- [ ] PLAN
- [ ] SOLVE
- [ ] CHECK

_____ concert DVDs

Identifying Patterns

PLUG IN Odd and Even Numbers

Odd numbers have 1, 3, 5, 7, or 9 in the ones place.

Even numbers have 0, 2, 4, 6, or 8 in the ones place.

17 is odd because after putting the 17 shapes into groups of 2 there is 1 shape left over.

10 is even because all 10 shapes can be put into groups of 2 with no shapes left over.

Words to Know

odd number
a number with 1, 3, 5, 7, or 9 in the ones place

1<u>3</u>

even number
a number with 0, 2, 4, 6, or 8 in the ones place

1<u>8</u>

DISCUSS How do you know if 20 is an odd or even number?

A You can sort objects to find if a number is odd or even.

DO

❶ Sort the squares into groups of 2.

❷ Count the squares. Write the number.

❸ Write *odd* or *even*.

number of squares: _____

The number is _____.

B You can look at the ones digit to tell if a number is odd or even.

DO

16

Tens	Ones
1	6

1 Make a place-value chart.

2 Look at the ones digit.

3 Write *odd* or *even*.

16 is an _____ number.

I remember! An equation uses an = sign to show equal quantities.

C You can write an equation to show an even number.

DO

1 Count the number of squares in one row. Write the number.

2 Count the number of squares in the other row. Write the number.

3 Add. Write the sum.

4 Write *odd* or *even*.

___**7**___ + 7 = _____

The number ___**14**___ is an _____ number.

PRACTICE

Sort the objects into groups of 2. Write the number. Write *odd* or *even*.

1

Number of stars: _____

The number is _____.

Look at the place-value chart. Write *odd* or *even*.

2

12

Tens	Ones
1	2

The number is _____.

Count the squares in each row. Add to find the sum. Write *odd* or *even*.

3

_____ + _____ = _____

The number _____ is an _____ number.

Multiplication and Division Facts

Multiplication is the same as repeated addition. **Division** is the same as repeated subtraction.

★ ★ ★ ★
★ ★ ★ ★
★ ★ ★ ★

Multiplication:

$3 \times 4 = 4 + 4 + 4$ $3 \times 4 = 12$

Division:

$12 \div 3 = 12 - 3 - 3 - 3 - 3$ $12 \div 3 = 4$

You can use a multiplication table to help you multiply and divide.

×	0	1	2	3	4	5
0	0	0	0	0	0	0
1	0	1	2	3	4	5
2	0	2	4	6	8	10
3	0	3	6	9	12	15
4	0	4	8	12	16	20
5	0	5	10	15	20	25

You can add or subtract the same amount each time.

Multiplication and division are inverse operations.

Words to Know

multiplication
combining equal groups

division
making equal groups

DISCUSS   How does a multiplication table help you multiply?

A You can use repeated addition to multiply.

DO

① Count the squares in each row.

② Write the numbers to complete the addition sentence.

③ Add. Write the sum.

④ Write the multiplication.

$\underline{\quad 6 \quad} + \underline{\qquad} + \underline{\qquad} = \underline{\qquad}$

$\underline{\quad 3 \quad} \times \underline{\qquad} = \underline{\qquad}$

B You can use repeated subtraction to divide.

When I use repeated subtraction, I subtract the same number each time until I get to 0.

❶ Count the total number of squares. Write the number.

❷ Count the number of squares in each row. Write the numbers.

❸ Subtract. Write the difference.

❹ Write the division.

<u> 8 </u> – <u>   </u> – <u>   </u> = <u>   </u>

<u>   </u> ÷ <u> 4 </u> = <u>   </u>

DISCUSS What multiplication fact can you use to check your answer to 8 ÷ 2? Explain.

PRACTICE

Use repeated addition to multiply.

❶

<u>   </u> + <u>   </u> + <u>   </u> + <u>   </u> + <u>   </u> = <u>   </u>

<u>   </u> × <u>   </u> = <u>   </u>

Use repeated subtraction to divide.

❷

<u> 15 </u> – <u>   </u> – <u>   </u> – <u>   </u> = <u>   </u>

<u>   </u> ÷ <u> 5 </u> = <u>   </u>

A number **pattern** is a series of numbers that follows a rule.

Each **product** in this pattern follows the same rule. The rule is to add 2.

$2 \times 1 = 2$
$2 \times 2 = 4$
$2 \times 3 = 6$
$2 \times 4 = 8$

2, 4, 6, 8

Each product increases by 2.

Patterns can use any operation. Here's a division pattern.

$12 \div 3 = 4$
$9 \div 3 = 3$
$6 \div 3 = 2$
$3 \div 3 = 1$

Each **quotient** is 1 less than the quotient before it.

4, 3, 2, 1

The quotient decreases by 1.

The numbers in a pattern change by following a rule.

$+4 \quad +4 \quad +4 \quad +4$
4, 8, 12, 16, 20,...

The numbers increase by 4. The rule is to add 4.

I can add 4 to the last number to find the next number in this pattern.

pattern	**product**	**quotient**
a series of numbers that follows a rule	the answer when numbers are multiplied	the answer when numbers are divided

DISCUSS Explain why the product of any number multiplied by 2 is always even.

LESSON LINK

PLUG IN	POWER UP	GO!

Numbers are either odd or even. Odd and even numbers form patterns.

Odd: 1, 3, 5, 7, 9, 11, 13, ...

Even: 2, 4, 6, 8, 10, 12, ...

Multiplication and division are related. You can use repeated addition to multiply and repeated subtraction to divide.

$2 + 2 + 2 + 2 + 2 = 10$
$5 \times 2 = 10$
$10 - 2 - 2 - 2 - 2 - 2 = 0$
$10 \div 2 = 5$

I see! A pattern follows a rule. After I find the rule, I can find the next number in the pattern.

> Multiplication is the same as repeated addition.

WORK TOGETHER

Use a multiplication table to help you find the rule.

12, 18, 24, 30, 36, …

- The numbers in the pattern increase by 6.
- The rule is to add 6.

×	0	1	2	3	4	5	6
0	0	0	0	0	0	0	0
1	0	1	2	3	4	5	6
2	0	2	4	6	8	10	**12**
3	0	3	6	9	12	15	**18**
4	0	4	8	12	16	20	**24**
5	0	5	10	15	20	25	**30**
6	0	6	**12**	**18**	**24**	**30**	**36**

$2 \times 6 = \mathbf{12}$
$3 \times 6 = \mathbf{18}$
$4 \times 6 = \mathbf{24}$
$5 \times 6 = \mathbf{30}$
$6 \times 6 = \mathbf{36}$

+6 +6 +6 +6
12, 18, 24, 30, 36,…

> **Multiplication Table** can be found on p. 229.

A Use the multiplication table to help you find the rule of the pattern.

DO   8, 16, 24, 32, 40, …

1. See if the numbers increase or decrease.
2. Find how the numbers change.
3. Write the rule.
4. Write the next number.

The numbers __**increase**__.

$8 + \underline{\hspace{2em}} = 16$ $16 + \underline{\hspace{2em}} = 24$

$24 + \underline{\hspace{2em}} = 32$ $32 + \underline{\hspace{2em}} = 40$

The rule is to _____.

The next number is _____.

B Use the multiplication table to help you find the rule of the pattern.

DO   56, 49, 42, 35, 28, …

1. See if the numbers increase or decrease.
2. Find how the numbers change.
3. Write the rule.
4. Write the next number.

The numbers __**decrease**__.

$56 - \underline{\hspace{2em}} = 49$ $49 - \underline{\hspace{2em}} = 42$

$42 - \underline{\hspace{2em}} = 35$ $35 - \underline{\hspace{2em}} = 28$

The rule is to _____.

The next number is _____.

DISCUSS
Tyrone wants to find the next number in the pattern
14, 21, 28, 35, . . .

What is the rule? _____   What is the next number? _____

PRACTICE

Complete the pattern. Write the rule for the pattern. Write the next number.

1 27, 36, 45, 54, 63, . . .

The numbers __increase__.

27 + __9__ = 36   36 + _____ = 45

45 + _____ = 54   54 + _____ = 63

The rule is to add _____.

The next number is _____.

2 36, 32, 28, 24, 20, . . .

The numbers __decrease__.

36 − _____ = 32   32 − _____ = 28

28 − _____ = 24   24 − _____ = 20

The rule is to _____.

The next number is _____.

3 9, 12, 15, 18, 21, . . .

The numbers _____.

9 + __3__ = 12   12 + _____ = 15

15 + _____ = 18   18 + _____ = 21

The rule is to _____.

The next number is _____.

Find each product. Write the pattern of the products. Describe the rule.

4 3 × 4 = _____

4 × 4 = _____

5 × 4 = _____

6 × 4 = _____

_____, _____, _____, _____

_____

5 5 × 9 = _____

4 × 9 = _____

3 × 9 = _____

2 × 9 = _____

_____, _____, _____, _____

_____

Use a pattern to help you solve.

6 There are 9 tennis balls in cans. There are 3 balls in each can. How many cans are there? _____

Is the quotient odd or even? _____

7 There are 8 bicycles in the shop. Each has 2 wheels. How many wheels are there? _____

Is the product odd or even? _____

> I can use a pattern to find the quotient in word problems, too.

DISCUSS **See the Pattern**

Marisa noticed a pattern in products of 9. Complete to show more of the pattern.

9 × 2 = **18**, and 1 + 8 = 9

9 × 3 = **27**, and 2 + 7 = 9

9 × 4 = **36**, and _____ + _____ = _____

9 × 5 = _____, and _____ + _____ = _____

9 × 6 = _____, and _____ + _____ = _____

9 × 7 = _____, and _____ + _____ = _____

What pattern do you see in the sum of the digits in the products of 9?

HINT
Add 9 to each product. If the sum of the digits is not 9, try adding again.

PROBLEM SOLVING

GETTING IN SHAPE

READ Jim does 20 sit-ups one day. He does 25, 30, and 35 the next 3 days. If the pattern continues, how many sit-ups will Jim do on the fifth day?

PLAN • What is the problem asking you to find?

You need to find the number of sit-ups Jim will do on the _____ day

• What do you need to know to solve the problem?

How many sit-ups does Jim do each day? _____

• How can you find the number of sit-ups?

Find the rule. Then find the next number in the pattern.

> I see! If my work is correct, the pattern is the same when I add or subtract.

SOLVE Find the rule.

$20 + 5 = 25$ $25 + 5 = 30$ $30 + 5 = 35$

The rule is to _____.

Find the next number in the pattern.

35 ◯ _____ = _____

CHECK Solve the pattern by subtracting.

_____ $- 5 = 35$ $35 - 5 =$ _____ $30 - 5 =$ _____ $25 - 5 =$ _____

Jim will do _____ sit-ups on the fifth day.

PRACTICE

Use the problem-solving steps to help you.

Once I know the rule, I can continue the pattern.

1 Amanda made a design using shapes. She used 4 circles, 6 squares, 8 circles, and 10 squares. If the pattern continues, how many circles will Amanda use next?

CHECKLIST
- [ ] READ
- [ ] PLAN
- [ ] SOLVE
- [ ] CHECK

2 Eric had 36 pencils. After giving pencils to some friends, he had 30, then 24, then 18 pencils left. If the pattern continues, how many pencils will he have left after sharing with two more friends?

CHECKLIST
- [ ] READ
- [ ] PLAN
- [ ] SOLVE
- [ ] CHECK

3 Ling picked two numbers that have an even sum and an odd product. The product is greater than 10 and less than 20. If one of the numbers is 5, what is the other number?

CHECKLIST
- [ ] READ
- [ ] PLAN
- [ ] SOLVE
- [ ] CHECK

Telling Time

PLUG IN   Time to the Nearest 5 Minutes

A clock is used to tell time. The **hour hand** is the shorter hand.

The hour hand is between 9 and 10, so it is past 9 o'clock.

It takes 5 minutes for the **minute hand** to move from number to number.

Each number shows 5 minutes. It is 9:05.

Using A.M. and P.M. helps you know if it is day or night.

I see! It is 8:35 at night, or 8:35 P.M.

Words to Know

| **hour hand** the shorter hand | **minute hand** the longer hand | **A.M.** times from midnight to noon | **P.M.** times from noon to midnight |

DISCUSS   Mia says that when the minute hand on a clock is pointing to the 6 it is 30 minutes past the hour. Do you agree or disagree?

A Write what time it is on the clock.

DO

❶ Look at the hour hand.

❷ Look at the minute hand.

❸ Write the time.

The hour hand is between ___**9**___ and _____.

The minute hand points to the _____.

The time is _____:_____.

B You can write the time using A.M. or P.M.

I do homework after school. That's between noon and midnight.

DO

❶ Look at the activity.

❷ Look at the hour.

❸ Look at the minute.

❹ Write the time.

The time is _____:_____ _____.

PRACTICE

Write what time it is.

1

The hour hand is between __11__ and _____.

The minute hand points to the _____.

The time is _____:_____.

Write the time using A.M. or P.M.

2

The time is _____:_____ _____.

Adding and Subtracting Whole Numbers

When adding or subtracting whole numbers, line up the numbers by place value.

$$28 + 48$$

$$53 - 29$$

Adding means to put together and subtracting means to take away.

Add each column.

```
   1
   2 8
 + 4 8
 -----
   7 6
```

Add the ones.

$8 + 8 = 16$ ones

Regroup 16 ones as

1 ten 6 ones.

Add the tens.

$1 + 2 + 4 = 7$

There are 7 tens.

The sum is 76.

Subtract each column.

```
   4 13
   5̶ 3̶
 - 2 9
 -----
   2 4
```

Regroup 5 tens as

4 tens 10 ones.

Subtract the ones.

$13 - 9 = 4$ ones

Subtract the tens.

$4 - 2 = 2$

There are 2 tens.

The difference is 24.

DISCUSS Why can you regroup 10 ones as 1 ten?

A You can use what you know about place value to add.

DO Add $39 + 56$.

❶ Line up the addends by place value.

❷ Add the ones. Regroup.

❸ Add the tens.

❹ Write the sum.

```
   3 9
 + 5 6
 -----
 [   ] 5
```

If there aren't enough ones to subtract, I need to regroup.

B You can use what you know about place value to subtract.

Subtract 70 − 14.

1. Line up the numbers by place value.

2. Subtract the ones. Regroup if needed.

3. Subtract the tens.

4. Write the difference.

$$\begin{array}{r} 7\ 0 \\ -\ 1\ 4 \\ \hline \square\ \square \end{array}$$

DISCUSS

Morgan says the difference of 62 − 49 = 23.
Is Morgan correct? What can you tell Morgan about her work?

PRACTICE

Add to find the sum.

1 60 + 32

2 187 + 245

Subtract to find the difference.

3 74 − 35

4 520 − 208

The clock shows 2:25.

In one minute, the minute hand moves from one mark to the next. The clock shows 2:38.

You can use subtraction to find **elapsed time**.

start time: 2:25
end time: 2:38

$$\begin{array}{r} 2:38 \\ -\ 2:25 \\ \hline 0:13 \end{array}$$

I know! I can skip count by 5s to tell the time.

Got it! From 2:35, I count on by 1s.

I get it! So, 13 minutes passed.

Words to Know

elapsed time
the time that passes between the start of an activity and the end of an activity

DISCUSS How many minutes are there in an hour? _____

LESSON LINK

PLUG IN ▶ **POWER UP** ▶ **GO!**

You can use a clock to tell time to the nearest 5 minutes.

3:30

Adding and subtracting can help you solve time problems.

$$\begin{array}{r} 15 \\ +\ 20 \\ \hline 35 \end{array} \qquad \begin{array}{r} 60 \\ -\ 20 \\ \hline 40 \end{array}$$

I get it! I can use a clock to tell time. I can add and subtract to find how much time has passed.

WORK TOGETHER

Use a number line to find elapsed time.

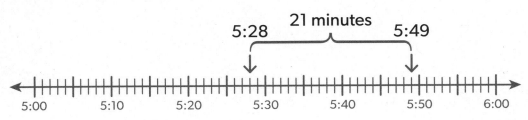

- The number line shows the 60 minutes from 5:00 to 6:00.
- The start time is 5:28. The end time is 5:49.
- Count on from 5:28 to 5:49.
- The elapsed time is 21 minutes.

> Use Blank Number Lines to find the elapsed time.
> Draw to show your work.

> **Blank Number Lines** can be found on p. 231.

A Find the elapsed time.

DO   start time: 4:11   end time: 4:54

> I can use a number line to model elapsed time.

1 Label every 10 minutes on the number line.

2 Find and label 4:11 and 4:54.

3 Count on from 4:11 to 4:54.

4 Write the elapsed time.

elapsed time: _____ minutes

> I can use subtraction to check the answer.

DISCUSS Aidan read from 2:39 to 2:56. He says he read for 27 minutes. Is Aidan correct? How can he check his answer?

PRACTICE

Write the time shown on the clock.

1

6: _____

2

_____ : _____

HINT
The hour hand is the shorter hand.

3

_____ : _____

4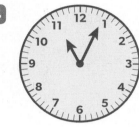

_____ : _____

Write how much time has passed.

5

Start

End

7:21   7:53

REMEMBER
You can use subtraction to find elapsed time.

$$
\begin{array}{r}
7{:}53 \\
-\ \boxed{} \\
\hline
\boxed{}
\end{array}
$$

elapsed time: _____

Write how much time has passed.

6

Start   End

1:34   1:49

elapsed time: _____

Solve.

7 A baseball game started at 6:18. The first inning lasted 17 minutes. What time did the first inning end? _____

8 Brianna started walking at 9:08. She walked for 21 minutes. What time did she stop walking? _____

I'm going to model the problem on a number line.

Look for a Pattern

Mr. Garcia made a list of some times. Fill in the missing times.

1:00, 1:15, 1:30, _____, 2:00, 2:15

10:35, 10:40, 10:45, 10:50, _____

4:06, 4:14, 4:22, _____, 4:38

How can addition and subtraction help you find the missing numbers?

HINT
You can use addition or subtraction to find the missing numbers.

PROBLEM SOLVING

BAKING COOKIES

READ

Madeline placed some cookies in the oven at 5:13. The cookies need to bake for 18 minutes. What time should Madeline take the cookies out of the oven?

PLAN

• What is the problem asking you to find?

You need to find the _____ when Madeline should take the cookies out of the oven.

• What do you need to know to solve the problem?

What time were the cookies placed in the oven? _____

How long do the cookies need to bake? _____

• How can you find the end time?

You can use addition or a number line.

SOLVE

Write the addition problem.

5:13 + _____ = _____

CHECK

Show the problem another way.
Use a number line.

Madeline should take the cookies out of the oven at _____.

PRACTICE

Use the problem-solving steps to help you.

I can use a number line to check my answers.

1 Lou rode the bus from 4:05 P.M. to 4:28 P.M. How many minutes was Lou on the bus?

CHECKLIST
- [ ] READ
- [ ] PLAN
- [ ] SOLVE
- [ ] CHECK

2 Caitlyn began practicing piano at 4:07. She practiced for 24 minutes. What time did Caitlyn stop practicing?

CHECKLIST
- [ ] READ
- [ ] PLAN
- [ ] SOLVE
- [ ] CHECK

3 It takes Andrew 25 minutes to get ready for school. His bus arrives at 8:50. What is the latest Andrew can begin getting ready for school?

CHECKLIST
- [ ] READ
- [ ] PLAN
- [ ] SOLVE
- [ ] CHECK

Problem Solving with Mass and Capacity

PLUG IN Mass

Mass measures how much matter an object has.

Grams (g) are used to measure the mass of lighter objects.

Kilograms (kg) are used to measure the mass of heavier objects.

Look! The scale is even, so it is balanced.

The mass of the feather is 1 gram.

The mass of the math book is 1 kilogram.

Words to Know

mass	gram (g)	kilogram (kg)
the measure of how much matter an object has	the unit used to measure the mass of lighter objects	the unit used to measure the mass of heavier objects

 DISCUSS Would you use grams or kilograms to measure the mass of a bicycle? Explain.

A You can look at an object to decide the better estimate of its mass.

DO Estimate the mass of a piece of chalk.

1. Look at the chalk.

2. Decide if the object is light or heavy.

3. Estimate the mass.

4. Circle the better estimate.

The object is _____.

5 grams or 50 grams

B You can use a balance scale to measure mass.

 Find the mass of the golf ball.

1 Look at the weights on the right side of the scale.

2 Add to find the mass of the golf ball.

3 Write the mass.

Remember to count all of the weights.

The mass of the weights is
10 + _____ + _____ + _____,
or _____ grams.

The mass of the golf ball is _____ grams.

PRACTICE

Circle the better estimate of the mass.

1 Mr. Shay is wearing a baseball cap. Estimate the mass of the baseball cap.

5 grams or 50 grams

Use the scale to write the mass.

2

The mass of the cat is _____ kilograms.

Liquid volume or **capacity** measures how much liquid a container can hold.

Milliliters (mL) are used to measure the volume of smaller containers.

Liters (L) are used to measure the volume of larger containers.

50 mL
40 mL
30 mL
20 mL
10 mL

1 liter

OK! The measuring cup contains about 50 milliliters of water.

An eyedropper can hold about 1 milliliter of water.

This bottle can hold about 1 liter of water.

Words to Know

liquid volume or **capacity**	**milliliter (mL)**	**liter (L)**
the amount of liquid a container can hold	the unit used to measure the liquid volume of smaller containers	the unit used to measure the liquid volume of larger containers

 DISCUSS   Would you use milliliters or liters to measure the liquid volume of a glass of orange juice? Explain.

A You can look at a container to decide the better estimate of its liquid volume.

DO   Estimate the liquid volume.

❶ Look at the container.

❷ Decide if it could hold a *little* or a *lot* of water.

❸ Estimate the liquid volume.

❹ Circle the better estimate.

The cooking pot could hold a _____ of water.

3 milliliters or 3 liters

Find the mark that lines up with the liquid.

B You can use a measuring cup to find the liquid volume of a container.

DO Find the liquid volume.

❶ Each mark on the measuring cup is 10 milliliters.

❷ Read the mark at the top of the liquid.

❸ Write the liquid volume.

50 mL
40 mL
30 mL
20 mL
10 mL

The liquid volume is _____ milliliters.

DISCUSS Joseph says the liquid volume of a small drinking glass should be measured in liters. What can you tell Joseph about his statement?

PRACTICE

Circle the better estimate of the liquid volume.

1

220 milliliters or 220 liters

2

4 milliliters or 4 liters

Write the liquid volume.

3

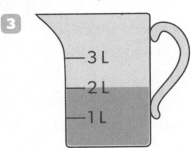

3 L
2 L
1 L

The liquid volume is _____ liters.

Problem Solving with Mass and Capacity

Word problems may ask for information about mass or liquid volume.

How much greater is the mass of Ella's book than Daniel's book?

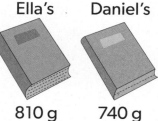

Ella's   Daniel's

810 g   740 g

Find the information that relates to the mass of the books.

The mass of Ella's book is 810 grams.

The mass of Daniel's book is 740 grams.

Use subtraction to solve the problem.

$$\begin{array}{r} \overset{7\ 11}{\cancel{8}\cancel{1}0} \\ -\ 7\ 4\ 0 \\ \hline 7\ 0 \end{array}$$

I need to know the mass of each book.

Ella's book is 70 grams more than Daniel's book.

DISCUSS How can you solve word problems that involve mass or liquid volume?

LESSON LINK

PLUG IN

Mass tells how much matter an object has.

5g

POWER UP

Liquid volume measures the liquid in a container.

50 mL
40 mL
30 mL
20 mL
10 mL

GO!

I know! I can solve word problems involving mass and liquid volume.

WORK TOGETHER

Use the information in the problem and the picture to help you.

- Write the amount of each juice to be mixed.
- Decide on the operation to use to solve the problem.
- Find the total milliliters of juice.

I can look for key words to help solve problems.

Seth wants to mix 425 milliliters of orange juice with the grapefruit juice in the pitcher. How many milliliters of juice will Seth have after he mixes them together?

Orange juice: 425 milliliters

Grapefruit juice: 300 milliliters

Use addition. 425 + 300 = 725

Seth will have 725 milliliters of juice.

A Use the information in the problem to solve. Show your work.

 DO

❶ Find the liquid volume of each bottle of water.

❷ Multiply to find how many liters in all.

❸ Solve the problem.

Luke bought eight 2-liter bottles of water. How many liters of water did Luke buy in all?

liquid volume of each bottle of water: _____ liters

_____ × _____ liters = _____ liters

Luke bought _____ of water in all.

I can multiply to find the total.

 DISCUSS

Mackenzie has four 2-liter bottles of juice. She says she has 6 liters of juice. What can you tell Mackenzie about her measurement?

PRACTICE

Solve.

1 Last week, Gavin drank 1 liter of water every day. How many liters of water did he drink last week?

7 × _____ liter = _____ liters

Gavin drank _____ liters of water last week.

2 Megan's backpack is 4 kilograms. Zoe's backpack is 1 kilogram less than Megan's backpack. What is the mass of Zoe's backpack?

Megan   Zoe

4 kilograms   ? kilograms

_____ kilograms − _____ kilogram = _____ kilograms

The mass of Zoe's backpack is _____ kilograms.

3 Mrs. Davis has 12 milliliters of liquid plant food. She feeds an equal amount to 3 plants. Mrs. Davis uses all of the liquid plant food. How much plant food does she feed each plant?

_____ milliliters ÷ __**3**__ = _____ milliliters

Mrs. Davis fed each plant _____ milliliters of liquid plant food.

4 Sean has 2 pencils. One has a mass of 42 grams. The other one has a mass of 56 grams. What is the total mass of the two pencils?

_____ grams + _____ grams = _____ grams

The total mass of the pencils is _____ grams.

> I have to find the operation needed to solve the problem.

Solve.

5 The total mass of 4 packets of sugar is 8 grams. Each packet of sugar has the same mass. What is the mass of each packet of sugar?   _____ grams

6 A 2-liter drink is shared equally between 2 friends. How many liters does each friend get?   _____ liter

7 In the morning, Lilly puts 500 milliliters of water into a birdbath. In the afternoon, 175 milliliters are left. How much water did the birds drink?   _____

8 Box A has a mass of 12 kilograms. Box B has a mass of 17 kilograms. How much greater is the mass of Box B than the mass of Box A?   _____

DISCUSS

Apply Mathematical Ideas to Real-World Situations

Noah buys a bottle of apple juice and Jordan buys a bottle of grape juice. Jordan says his bottle holds less juice. Is Jordan correct? Explain.

Apple Juice 1 liter

Grape Juice 1 liter

Explain why containers can have the same capacity even though they have different shapes.

HINT
Compare the capacity of each bottle.

PROBLEM SOLVING

SERVING LEMONADE

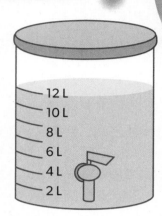

READ Anna divides 12 liters of lemonade equally into 6 smaller containers. How much lemonade does she put into each smaller container?

12 L
10 L
8 L
6 L
4 L
2 L

PLAN • What is the problem asking you to find?

You need to find how much _____ Anna put into each smaller container.

• What do you need to know to solve the problem?

What is the amount of lemonade in the pitcher? _____

How many smaller containers are there? _____

• How can you find the amount of lemonade Anna put into each container?

You can _____.

SOLVE Write the division problem. Find the quotient.

_____ liters ÷ _____ = _____ liters

CHECK Show the problem another way.

Use repeated subtraction. Subtract 6.

_____ liters − _____ liters = _____ liters

_____ liters − _____ liters = _____ liters

You subtracted 6 two times.

Anna put _____ liters of lemonade into each smaller container.

PRACTICE

Use the problem-solving steps to help you.

I can draw a picture to help me solve the problem.

1 Christopher's puppy gained 3 kilograms this year. The puppy's mass is now 21 kilograms. What was his mass last year?

CHECKLIST
- [ ] READ
- [ ] PLAN
- [ ] SOLVE
- [ ] CHECK

2 18 liters of milk was divided equally into 9 bottles. How much milk was put into each bottle?

CHECKLIST
- [ ] READ
- [ ] PLAN
- [ ] SOLVE
- [ ] CHECK

3 Benjamin buys two baseballs. The mass of each baseball is 142 grams. What is the combined mass of the two baseballs?

CHECKLIST
- [ ] READ
- [ ] PLAN
- [ ] SOLVE
- [ ] CHECK

Picture Graphs

PLUG IN Making a Picture Graph

A **picture graph** is a way to show **data** using pictures.
The **key** shows what each picture stands for.
Count to find how many students chose each fruit.

Favorite Fruit

Apple	★ ★ ★
Banana	★ ★ ★ ★ ★
Orange	★ ★
Pear	★

Key: Each ★ = 1 student

This graph is about favorite fruit.

Each star stands for 1 student.

3 chose apples,
5 chose bananas,
2 chose oranges,
and 1 chose pears.

 Words to Know

| **picture graph** a graph that uses symbols to show data | **data** numerical information | **key** tells how many each symbol represents |

DISCUSS How can you find the total number of students represented in the data?

A You can read a picture graph to answer questions about data.

DO How many students chose art?

❶ Find the row for Art in the graph.

❷ Count the number of book symbols.

❸ Look at the key to see what each symbol represents.

❹ Write the number of students.

Favorite Subject

Art	📗 📗
Math	📗 📗 📗 📗 📗
Reading	📗 📗 📗
Science	📗 📗 📗

Key: Each 📗 = 1 student

There are __2__ books in the row for Art.

_____ students chose art.

B You can complete a picture graph to match the data in a table.

DO

1. Look at the key in the picture graph.

2. Find how many symbols to draw for each activity.

3. Fill in the picture graph.

Favorite Activity

Activity	Number of Students
Painting	6
Drawing	3
Swimming	7
Jogging	4

Favorite Activity

Painting	
Drawing	
Swimming	
Jogging	

Key: Each ■ = 1 student

PRACTICE

Use the Favorite Activity picture graph to answer questions 1–3.

1. How many students chose drawing as their favorite activity?

   _____

2. How many more students chose swimming than jogging?

   _____

3. Which activity was chosen by the fewest students?

   _____

The table and picture graph show information about students' favorite vacation spots. Complete the picture graph to match the data in the table.

4.

Favorite Vacation Spot

Vacation Spot	Number of Students
Beach	11
Lake	2
Mountains	4
National Park	3

Favorite Vacation Spot

Beach	
Lake	
Mountains	
National Park	

Key: Each ■ = 1 student

Adding and Subtracting Whole Numbers

When adding or subtracting whole numbers, line up the numbers by place value.

$$75 + 15$$ $$60 - 25$$

Adding means to join and subtracting means to take away.

Add each column.

$$
\begin{array}{r}
1 \\
7\,5 \\
+\,1\,5 \\
\hline
9\,0
\end{array}
$$

Add the ones.

$$5 + 5 = 10 \text{ ones}$$

Regroup 10 ones as 1 ten 0 ones.

Add the tens.

$$1 + 7 + 1 = 9$$

There are 9 tens.

The sum is 90.

Subtract each column.

$$
\begin{array}{r}
5\;10 \\
\cancel{6}\,\cancel{0} \\
-\,2\,5 \\
\hline
3\,5
\end{array}
$$

Regroup 6 tens as 5 tens 10 ones.

Subtract the ones.

$$10 - 5 = 5 \text{ ones}$$

Subtract the tens.

$$5 - 2 = 3$$

There are 3 tens.

The difference is 35.

 DISCUSS   Why can you regroup 1 ten as 10 ones?

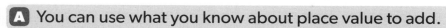

A You can use what you know about place value to add.

DO   Add 24 + 38.

1. Line up the addends by place value.
2. Add the ones. Regroup.
3. Add the tens.
4. Write the sum.

$$
\begin{array}{r}
2\,4 \\
+\,3\,8 \\
\hline
2
\end{array}
$$

> If there aren't enough ones to subtract, I need to regroup.

B You can use what you know about place value to subtract.

 Subtract 40 − 15.

1. Line up the numbers by place value.
2. Subtract the ones. Regroup if needed.
3. Subtract the tens.
4. Write the difference.

$$\begin{array}{r} 40 \\ -15 \\ \hline \end{array}$$

DISCUSS

Maria says the difference of 77 − 48 = 31.

Is Maria correct? What can you tell Maria about her work?

PRACTICE

Add to find the sum.

1 80 + 45

2 56 + 36

Subtract to find the difference.

3 82 − 56

4 70 − 35

Picture Graphs

Points Scored

Tigers	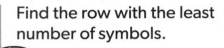
Bears	
Lions	
Cardinals	

Key: Each 🏈 = 2 points

Which team scored the fewest points? How many points did they score?

I can use the picture graph to answer the questions.

Find the row with the least number of symbols.

The Tigers scored the fewest points.

The key shows that each 🏈 stands for 2 points.

Multiply. 3 × 2 = 6

The Tigers scored 6 points.

DISCUSS Explain how to find the total number of points scored by all teams.

LESSON LINK

PLUG IN	**POWER UP**	**GO!**

Picture graphs help you to easily see data.

Eye Color

Blue	👁 👁
Green	👁 👁 👁 👁
Brown	👁 👁 👁
Hazel	👁

Key: Each 👁 = 1 student

Adding and subtracting can help you compare data.

Green eyes   4
Blue eyes   − 2
                    ‾‾‾
                     2

There are 2 fewer students with blue eyes than green eyes.

I get it! I can use addition and subtraction to answer questions about any picture graph.

I will draw 1 symbol for each group of 5 students.

WORK TOGETHER

Make a picture graph.

- The key shows that each symbol equals 5 students.

- Divide the number of students by 5 to find how many symbols to draw.

  Spring: $15 \div 5 = 3$
  Summer: $25 \div 5 = 5$
  Fall: $20 \div 5 = 4$
  Winter: $5 \div 5 = 1$

- Fill in the picture graph.

Favorite Season

Season	Number of Students
Spring	15
Summer	25
Fall	20
Winter	5

Favorite Season

Spring	■ ■ ■
Summer	■ ■ ■ ■ ■
Fall	■ ■ ■ ■
Winter	■

Key: Each ■ = 5 students

A You can make a picture graph to match the data in a table.

DO

① Use the key to find how many symbols to draw for each day.

② Divide each number in the table by the value of each symbol, 2.

③ Fill in the picture graph.

Orange Juice Sales

Day	Number of Glasses
Sunday	6
Monday	12
Tuesday	8
Wednesday	10

Orange Juice Sales

Sunday	
Monday	
Tuesday	
Wednesday	

Key: Each 🥛 = 2 glasses sold

B You can read the picture graph above to answer questions about the data.

DO

① Find the number of glasses sold on Monday and Sunday.

② Subtract.

③ Write the difference.

How many more glasses of orange juice were sold on Monday than on Sunday?

_____ − _____ = _____

_____ more glasses were sold on Monday.

DISCUSS

On Thursday, 16 glasses of orange juice were sold. How do you know the number of symbols to draw on the picture graph for Thursday?

What number times 2 equals 16?

PRACTICE

Use the Magazine Sales picture graph to answer questions 1–6.

Magazine Sales

Marla	▐ ▐ ▐ ▐ ▐
Adam	▐ ▐
Nate	▐ ▐ ▐ ▐
Claire	▐ ▐ ▐ ▐ ▐ ▐

Key: Each ▐ = 10 magazines sold

HINT
The key tells me to multiply each number of symbols by 10 to find each student's sales.

1 Who sold the greatest number of magazines? How many magazines did that

student sell? _____

2 How many magazines were sold in all? Show your work.

_____

3 How many more magazines did Nate sell than Adam?

_____

4 How many fewer magazines did Claire sell than Marla and Adam combined?

_____

5 Who sold more magazines combined, Marla and Nate or
Adam and Claire?

_____

REMEMBER
Some word problems are solved by using more than one step.

6 If each symbol represented 5 magazines, how many symbols would be needed

for Marla's row? _____

Make a picture graph to match the data in the table.

7

Favorite Food

Food	Number of Students
Pizza	10
Tacos	8
Hot Dogs	12
Salad	6

Favorite Food

Pizza	
Tacos	
Hot Dogs	
Salad	

Key: Each ■ = 2 students

Use the Favorite Food picture graph to answer questions 8–9.

Remember to look at the key!

8 Which food is the least favorite? How many students like that type of food? _____

9 How many more students like hot dogs than pizza? _____

 Represent Missing Data

In the picture graph, 5 ● represent 20 points.

Complete the missing information in the table and picture graph.

Points Scored

Player	Number of Points
Tao	24
Cho	
Mark	20
Ava	40

Points Scored

Tao	
Cho	●●●●●●●●
Mark	●●●●●
Ava	

What is the key of the picture graph? Explain your answer.

151

PROBLEM SOLVING

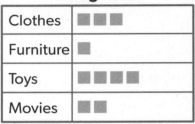

GARAGE SALE

READ Mrs. James kept track of the number of items she sold at a garage sale. How many toys were sold?

Garage Sale

Clothes	■ ■ ■
Furniture	■
Toys	■ ■ ■ ■
Movies	■ ■

Key: Each ■ = 5 items sold

PLAN • What is the problem asking you to find?

You need to find how many _____ were sold.

• What do you need to know to solve the problem?

How many symbols are shown in the row for toys? _____

What does each symbol represent? _____

• What should you do to find how many toys were sold?

You need to multiply or count.

SOLVE Multiply to find how many toys were sold.

___4___ × _____ = _____

CHECK Find the number of toys another way.
Skip count by 5s.

___5___, _____, _____, _____

There were _____ toys sold at the garage sale.

PRACTICE

Use the problem-solving steps to help you.

1 Don made this picture graph to show the number of jumping jacks he did each day from Monday through Thursday.

How many more jumping jacks did Don do on Wednesday than Monday?

Jumping Jacks

Monday	▪ ▪ ▪ ▪ ▪
Tuesday	▪ ▪ ▪ ▪
Wednesday	▪ ▪ ▪ ▪ ▪ ▪
Thursday	▪ ▪ ▪ ▪ ▪ ▪ ▪ ▪

Key: Each ▪ = 10 jumping jacks

CHECKLIST
- [ ] READ
- [ ] PLAN
- [ ] SOLVE
- [ ] CHECK

2 Some students at Conway Elementary School made a picture graph to show the numbers of ribbons they sold during a school fund-raiser.

How many ribbons in all did the students sell?

Ribbon Sales

Jack	🎗🎗🎗🎗
Emily	🎗🎗🎗🎗🎗🎗🎗🎗
Kara	🎗🎗🎗
Miguel	🎗🎗🎗🎗🎗🎗

Key: Each 🎗 = 5 ribbons sold

CHECKLIST
- [ ] READ
- [ ] PLAN
- [ ] SOLVE
- [ ] CHECK

3 Mr. Ruiz made this picture graph to show some of his students' favorite shapes.

Which shape is liked by the most students? How many students like that shape?

Favorite Shape

Trapezoid	★ ★ ★ ★
Pentagon	★ ★ ★
Hexagon	★ ★
Octagon	★ ★ ★ ★ ★ ★

Key: Each = 2 students

CHECKLIST
- [ ] READ
- [ ] PLAN
- [ ] SOLVE
- [ ] CHECK

Bar Graphs

PLUG IN Adding and Subtracting with Data

How many more students chose reading than science? Use **data** from the **picture graph**. Each symbol stands for 2 votes.

Favorite Subject

Math	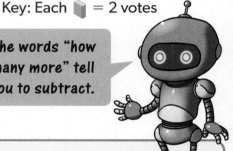
Science	
Reading	
Art	

Key: Each 🔋 = 2 votes

1. Reading has 9 symbols.
   $9 \times 2 = 18$
   So 18 students chose reading.

2. Science has 6 symbols.
   $6 \times 2 = 12$
   So 12 students chose science.

3. Subtract: $18 - 12 = 6$
   So 6 more students chose reading than science.

> The words "how many more" tell you to subtract.

Words to Know

data
numerical information

picture graph
uses pictures to show data

DISCUSS Will you get the same answer if you subtract the number of symbols first and then multiply? Explain.

A You can read the data on a picture graph to solve a problem.

DO Use the Favorite Subject graph. How many votes were there in all?

❶ There were 18 votes for reading and 12 for science. Find the number for math.

❷ Find the number of votes for art.

❸ Add the numbers for math, science, reading, and art.

Multiply: $5 \times 2 = 10$

So _____ students chose math.

Multiply: $4 \times 2 = 8$

So _____ students chose art.

_____ + _____ + _____ + _____ = _____

There were _____ votes in all.

B You can read the data on a picture graph to solve a problem.

DO How many more students chose orange juice than grapefruit juice?

1 Read the key.

2 Multiply to find the number of votes for orange juice.

3 Multiply to find the number of votes for grapefruit juice.

4 Subtract to find how many more students chose orange juice than grapefruit juice.

Favorite Juice

Apple	🥤🥤🥤🥤🥤
Orange	🥤🥤🥤🥤🥤🥤🥤🥤
Grapefruit	🥤🥤🥤🥤
Grape	🥤🥤🥤🥤🥤🥤

Key: Each 🥤 = 2 votes

Each symbol stands for _____ votes.

For orange juice, multiply by 2:

$2 \times 8 = 16$

So _____ students chose orange juice.

For grapefruit juice, multiply by 2:

$2 \times 4 = 8$

So _____ students chose grapefruit juice.

Subtract: _____ − _____ = _____ more

So _____ more students chose orange juice.

PRACTICE

Use the Favorite Color picture graph to solve each problem.

1 Find the number of students that chose each color. Fill in the totals on the lines to the right of the rows on the graph.

Favorite Color

Yellow	\ \ \ \ \ \ \ \	_____
Red	\ \ \ \ \	_____
Orange	\ \ \	_____
Blue	\ \ \ \ \ \	_____

Key: Each \ = 10 students

2 How many more students chose red than orange?

□ − □ = □ students

3 How many students were there in all?

□ + □ + □ + □ = □ students

Bar graphs use bars of different lengths to represent data. This graph shows the number of students who brought different snacks.

How many students in all brought snacks?

1. The bar for Muffin lines up with the 2 on the **scale**. So 2 students brought muffins.

2. The bar for Granola Bar lines up with the 6. So 6 students brought granola bars.

3. The bar for Apple lines up with the 3. So 3 students brought apples.

4. The bar for Pretzel lines up with 4. So 4 students brought pretzels.

5. Add to find the total:
   2 + 6 + 3 + 4 = 15

So 15 students in all brought snacks.

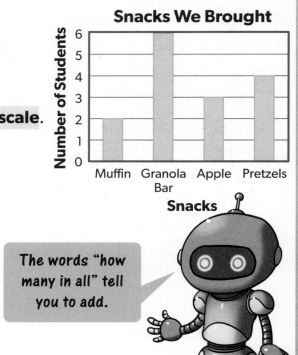

Snacks We Brought

The words "how many in all" tell you to add.

 Words to Know

bar graph
a graph that uses bars and a scale to show and compare data

scale
a series of numbers along one side of a graph that tells you the data

 DISCUSS How is a bar graph similar to a picture graph? How are they different?

A You need to read the data on a bar graph to solve a problem.

DO Use the Snacks We Brought graph. How many fewer students brought pretzels than granola bars?

❶ Find the number of students who brought pretzels.

There were ___**4**___ students who brought pretzels.

❷ Find the number of students who brought granola bars.

There were _____ students who brought granola bars.

❸ Decide which operation to use.

The words "how many fewer" tell you to _____.

_____ ◯ _____ = _____

❹ Find the answer.

So _____ fewer students brought pretzels than granola bars.

B You can make a bar graph to show data.

Bar graphs use bars to show the data.

DO   Make a bar graph to match the data in the table.

Favorite Zoo Animals

Animal	Number of Students
Giraffe	6
Zebra	4
Tiger	5
Monkey	6

1 Label the left side of the graph.

2 Label the names of the animals.

3 Use the number of students that voted for each animal to draw bars.

4 Make sure each bar lines up with the number shown on the bottom scale.

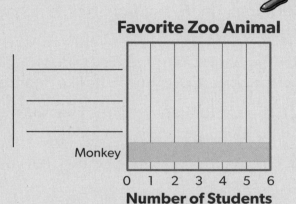

Favorite Zoo Animal

Monkey

0 1 2 3 4 5 6

Number of Students

DISCUSS   How do you know what numbers to use on the scale of a bar graph?

PRACTICE

1 Complete the bar graph to show the data in the table.

Our Pets

Pets	Number of Students
Bird	3
Fish	6
Cat	4
Dog	8

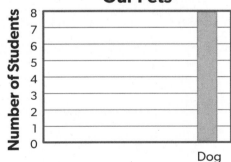

Our Pets

Number of Students

8
7
6
5
4
3
2
1
0

Dog

Use the Our Pets bar graph for questions 2 and 3.

2 How many students in all were asked about their pets?

_____ students

3 How many more students have a dog than a bird?

_____ students

Some bar graphs use a scale that is more than 1, such as 2, 5, or 10. This graph shows the number of students who voted for their favorite carnival game.

How many more students like the ring toss than balloon darts?

1. The bar for Ring Toss lines up with 25 on the scale. So 25 students like ring toss.

2. The bar for Balloon Darts lines up with 10. So 10 students like balloon darts.

3. The words "how many more" tell you to subtract: $25 - 10 = 15$

So 15 more students like ring toss than balloon darts.

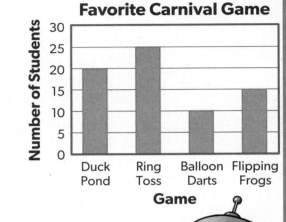

Favorite Carnival Game

I see! This bar graph has 4 categories and a scale of 5.

DISCUSS

If a scale of 10 was used for the Favorite Carnival Game graph, what numbers would be on the scale? How would you draw the bar for Ring Toss on the graph?

LESSON LINK

PLUG IN | **POWER UP** | **GO!**

Some problems are solved from data in a picture graph.

Favorite Ice Cream

Chocolate	🍦🍦🍦🍦
Vanilla	🍦🍦
Strawberry	🍦

Key: Each 🍦 = 1 student

$4 + 2 + 1 = 7$
7 students voted.

Bar graphs use bars of different lengths to show data.

Favorite Vegetable

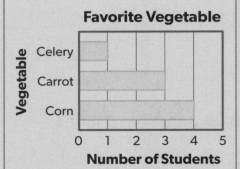

3 students like carrots best.

I get it! If I'm graphing greater numbers, I can use a scale greater than 1! Then, I can use the data to solve problems.

WORK TOGETHER

Make a bar graph for the data in the table.

1. Label the graph title, the categories on the bottom, and the scale. Use a scale of 2.

2. Use the number of students from the table to draw the bars.

3. If a number is between two numbers on the scale, put the top of the bar halfway between those two numbers.

Shoes We're Wearing

Type of Shoe	Boots	Slip-Ons	Sandals	Sneakers
Number of Students	8	7	3	12

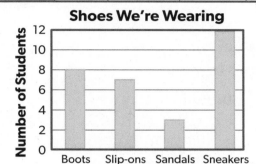

A Use the data in the table to make a bar graph.

DO

1. Label the title for the graph.

2. Label the scale on the left side of the graph. Use a scale of 2.

3. Label the categories on the bottom of the graph. Write the names of the categories.

4. Use the number of votes from the table for each insect to draw the bars.

Favorite Insect

Insect	Number of Votes
Butterfly	11
Ladybug	8
Dragonfly	3
Honeybee	2

 Axel and Tom asked 100 third graders to name their favorite TV show from 4 choices. Axel wants to use a scale of 2 to make a bar graph. Tom wants to use a scale of 10. Who do you agree with? Explain.

PRACTICE

Use the Our Favorite Sport graph for questions 1–3.

1 How many students voted for basketball?

_____ students

HINT
The bar is halfway between 12 and 14.

2 How many more students voted for baseball than soccer?

_____ students

3 How many students in all voted on their favorite sport?

_____ students

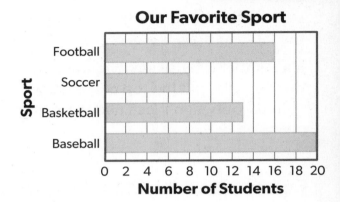

Our Favorite Sport

Use the Favorite Farm Animal graph for questions 4–6.

4 Which farm animal did 15 students vote for?

_____

5 How many students voted for horse and pig?

_____ students

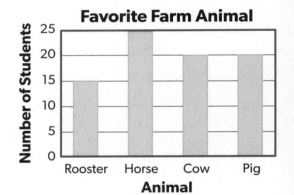

Favorite Farm Animal

6 How many fewer students voted for the rooster than for the cow?

_____ students

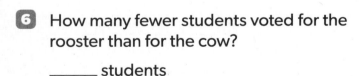

Use the data in the table to complete the bar graph.

7

Favorite Meat

Type of Meat	Number of Votes
Chicken	25
Beef	15
Fish	10
Pork	20

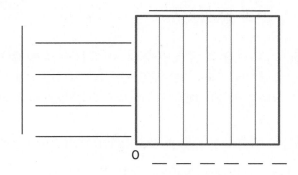

0

Use the Favorite Meat graph for questions 8 and 9.

8 How many students were asked to choose their favorite meat? _____

9 How many more students chose chicken than fish? _____

I add to find a total. I subtract to compare.

DISCUSS

Model Mathematics

With a partner, think of a subject for making a bar graph.

Write a question and make a list of 4 choices. Survey your classmates.

Use the data to make a bar graph.

How did you decide on a scale for your graph?

Write 2 problems about your graph. Exchange problems with your partner and solve each other's problems.

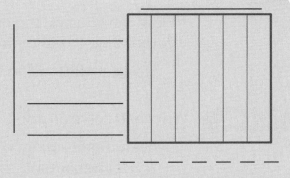

REMEMBER
Some bars may end between the numbers on the scale.

PROBLEM SOLVING

FIELD TRIP

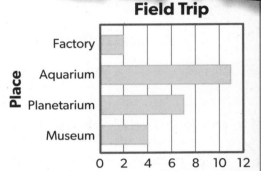

READ — Third graders voted for a place to go on a field trip. How many students voted for either the aquarium or the museum?

PLAN — • What is the problem asking you to find?

How many students voted for either the _____ or the _____.

Field Trip

Place: Factory, Aquarium, Planetarium, Museum

Number of Votes: 0 2 4 6 8 10 12

• What do you need to know to solve the problem?

Read each bar on the graph.

How many students voted to go to the aquarium? _____

How many students voted to go to the museum? _____

• How can you find the number of students who voted to go to either the aquarium or the museum?

You can add to find the total.

This bar graph has a scale of 2.

SOLVE — Write and solve an addition sentence.

students voting for aquarium ↓   students voting for museum ↓

_____ + _____ = _____

CHECK — Use subtraction to check addition.

_____ − _____ = _____

There were _____ students who voted to go to either the aquarium or the museum.

PRACTICE

Use the Favorite Camp Activity bar graph and the problem-solving steps to help you.

1 How many students voted for either fishing or hiking?

Favorite Camp Activity

CHECKLIST
- [ ] READ
- [ ] PLAN
- [ ] SOLVE
- [ ] CHECK

2 How many more students voted for swimming than painting?

CHECKLIST
- [ ] READ
- [ ] PLAN
- [ ] SOLVE
- [ ] CHECK

3 How many students voted in all?

CHECKLIST
- [ ] READ
- [ ] PLAN
- [ ] SOLVE
- [ ] CHECK

17 Line Plots

PLUG IN Understanding Line Plots

Line plots are used to show how **data** is grouped.

How many pencils are 4 inches long?

Pencils

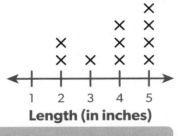

Length (in inches)

This line plot shows the lengths, in inches, of some pencils.

Each X stands for one pencil.

There are 3 Xs above the 4.

Pencils

1 2 3 4 5
Length (in inches)

So, there are 3 pencils that are each 4 inches long.

Words to Know

line plot
a graph that uses Xs and a number line to show data

data
numerical information

DISCUSS How can you find the total number of objects when reading a line plot?

A You can read a line plot to answer questions about data.

DO How many worms are 2 inches long?

❶ The line plot shows the length, in inches, of each worm. Each X stands for one worm.

❷ Find 2 on the number line. Count the number of Xs above 2.

❸ Write the number.

Worms

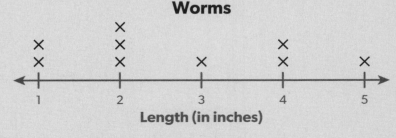

Length (in inches)

There are ___3___ Xs above 2 inches.

There are _____ worms that are 2 inches long.

B You can make a line plot to show data.

Not all lengths have Xs.

DO Make a line plot to show the data of Sticker Lengths.

1 The table shows the number of stickers for each length.

2 Make a number line from 1 to 5 inches.

3 Label the title and the number line.

4 Draw an X to represent each sticker.

Sticker Lengths

Length (in inches)	1	2	3	4	5
Number of Stickers	2	4	1	3	0

Sticker Lengths

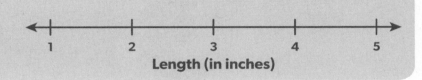

Length (in inches)

PRACTICE

Use the Sticker Lengths line plot to answer questions 1–3.

1 How many stickers are 2 inches long?

_____

2 What is the length of the longest sticker?

_____ inches

3 How many stickers are shorter than 3 inches?

_____

4 Abigail measured 10 butterflies. She made a table to show the measurements. Fill in the line plot to match the data in the table.

Butterfly Lengths

Length (in inches)	Number of Butterflies
1	0
2	3
3	2
4	4
5	1

Butterfly Lengths

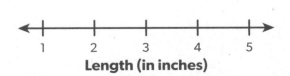

Length (in inches)

Fractions on a Number Line

| Number lines can be used to show **fractions**. | There are 4 equal parts from 0 to 1. | There are three $\frac{1}{4}$s between 0 and the point. |

$\frac{1}{4}$ $\frac{1}{4}$ $\frac{1}{4}$ $\frac{1}{4}$

0   1

This number line between 0 and 1 is divided into fourths.

Each part shows $\frac{1}{4}$ of the whole.

The point shows $\frac{3}{4}$.

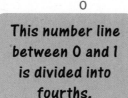

> **Words to Know** **fraction**
> a number that shows a part of a whole

DISCUSS
When modeling fractions on a number line from 0 to 1, how do you know which number to use as the denominator?

A You can show a fraction on a number line.

DO Draw a point to show $\frac{3}{6}$ on the number line.

❶ The denominator is 6. Find how many equal parts are from 0 to 1.

There are ___**6**___ equal parts from 0 to 1 on the number line.

❷ Find what fraction each part shows.

Each part shows _____ of the whole.

❸ The numerator is 3, so count 3 parts from 0.

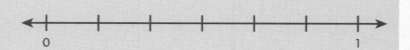

0   1

❹ Draw a point on the number line.

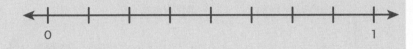
Count how many $\frac{1}{8}$s between 0 and the point.

B You can show a fraction on a number line.

DO Show the fraction $\frac{5}{8}$ on the number line.

1 The denominator is 8. Find how many equal parts are from 0 to 1.

There are ___**8**___ equal parts from 0 to 1 on the number line.

2 Find what fraction each part shows.

Each part shows _____ of the whole.

3 The numerator is 5, so count 5 parts from 0.

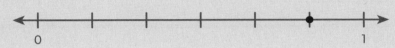

4 Draw a point on the number line.

DISCUSS Marcus says the point on this number line shows the fraction $\frac{5}{6}$. Is he correct? Explain.

PRACTICE

Show the fraction on the number line.

1 $\frac{1}{3}$

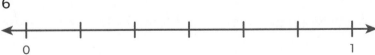

2 $\frac{4}{6}$

3 $\frac{3}{8}$

Sometimes we measure objects with a ruler to the nearest $\frac{1}{2}$ inch or $\frac{1}{4}$ inch.

This table shows the lengths of some bows.

Bow Lengths

Length (in inches)	Number of Bows
3	2
$3\frac{1}{2}$	4
4	2
$4\frac{1}{2}$	1
5	1

This line plot shows the same data as in the table. Each X represents 1 bow.

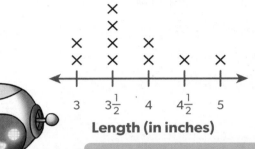

Bow Lengths

There are 6 bows that are shorter than 4 inches.

 DISCUSS How many bows are longer than 4 inches? Explain your answer.

LESSON LINK

PLUG IN ➤ **POWER UP** ➤ **GO!**

A line plot uses a number line and Xs to show data.

Erasers

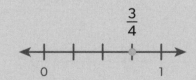

Length (in inches)

You can show fractions on a number line.

$\frac{3}{4}$

0   1

I get it! There are times when I will need to use fractions to show data on a line plot.

Each X stands for 1 stick.

WORK TOGETHER

Make a line plot to show the data in the table.

- The table shows the lengths of some sticks.
- Label a number line from 6 to 7 inches in fourths.
- Draw an X to represent each stick.
- Write a title and label the number line.

Stick Lengths

Length (in inches)	6	$6\frac{1}{4}$	$6\frac{2}{4}$	$6\frac{3}{4}$	7
Number of Sticks	1	0	3	4	2

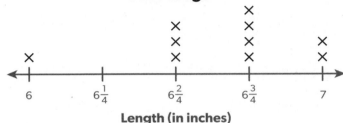

Stick Lengths

Length (in inches)

A You can make a line plot to show data.

DO Make a line plot to show the data of Crayon Lengths.

❶ The table shows the lengths of a number of crayons.

❷ Draw a number line from 3 to 4 inches in fourths.

❸ Label the title and the number line.

❹ Draw an X to represent each crayon.

Crayon Lengths

Length (in inches)	3	$3\frac{1}{4}$	$3\frac{2}{4}$	$3\frac{3}{4}$	4
Number of Crayons	3	0	4	1	2

Crayon Lengths

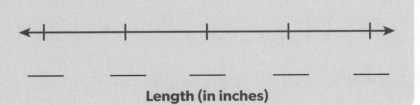

Length (in inches)

Caleb wants to know how many crayons were measured. How can he find the number of crayons that were measured? How many crayons were measured?

PRACTICE

Use the Bird Lengths line plot to answer questions 1–6.

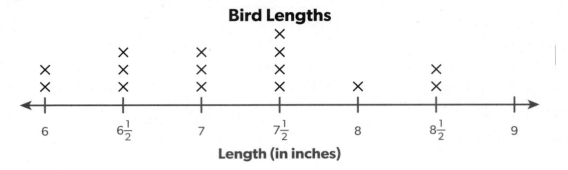

Bird Lengths

Length (in inches)

1 How many birds are $7\frac{1}{2}$ inches long?

_____ birds

2 What is the length of the shortest bird?

_____ inches

3 How many birds are longer than $6\frac{1}{2}$ inches?

_____ birds

4 How many birds are shorter than $6\frac{1}{2}$ inches?

_____ birds

5 What is the length of the longest bird?

_____ inches

6 How many birds were measured in all?

_____ birds

Jacob measured 10 leaves. He made a table to show the measurements.
Fill in the line plot to match the data in the table.

7

Leaf Lengths

Length (in inches)	Number of Leaves
4	2
$4\frac{1}{4}$	0
$4\frac{2}{4}$	3
$4\frac{3}{4}$	3
5	2

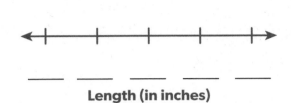

Leaf Lengths

Length (in inches)

Some lengths may not have any Xs.

Use the Leaf Lengths line plot to answer questions 8–9.

8 How many leaves are $4\frac{1}{4}$ inches long? _____ leaves

9 What is the difference in length between the longest leaf and the shortest leaf? _____ inch

Subtract to find the difference.

 Analyze the Data

Cho measured the lengths of some cards. She recorded her measurements in this table.

Card Lengths

Length (in inches)	3	$3\frac{1}{2}$	4	$4\frac{1}{2}$	5
Number of Cards	1	0	3	4	2

Are most of the cards longer or shorter than 4 inches? In a line plot, how many Xs would you draw above 4 inches? Explain your answer.

PROBLEM SOLVING

DINOSAUR BONES

READ

A scientist recorded the lengths of some dinosaur bones. The line plot shows the data. How many bones are $3\frac{1}{4}$ feet or longer?

Bone Lengths

Length (in feet)

PLAN

• What is the problem asking you to find?

You need to find how many _____ are $3\frac{1}{4}$ feet or longer.

• What do you need to know to solve the problem?

How many bones are $3\frac{1}{4}$ feet long? _____

How many bones are $3\frac{2}{4}$ feet long? _____

How many bones are $3\frac{3}{4}$ feet long? _____

How many bones are 4 feet long? _____

• What should you do to solve the problem?

You should add or count.

SOLVE

Add to find how many bones are $3\frac{1}{4}$ feet or longer.

_____ + _____ + _____ + _____ = _____

CHECK

Look at the line plot again.

Count the Xs above $3\frac{1}{4}$, $3\frac{2}{4}$, $3\frac{3}{4}$, and 4.

_____ bones are $3\frac{1}{4}$ feet or longer.

Bone Lengths

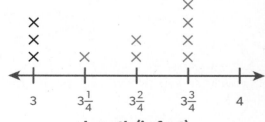

Length (in feet)

PRACTICE

Use the problem-solving steps to help you.

1 Cheryl measured 10 of her barrettes. She made this line plot to show the measurements.

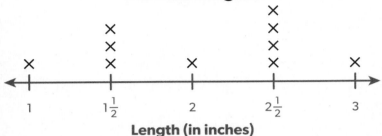

Barrette Lengths

Length (in inches)

How many barrettes are $1\frac{1}{2}$ inches long?

2 Steven measured some action figures. He made this line plot to show his data.

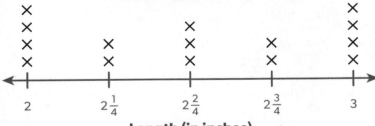

Action Figure Lengths

Length (in inches)

How many action figures did Steven measure?

3 Use the line plot in question 2. How many action figures are longer than $2\frac{2}{4}$ inches?

18 Perimeter

PLUG IN Measuring Figures

You can use squares to measure the lengths of the sides of a shape.

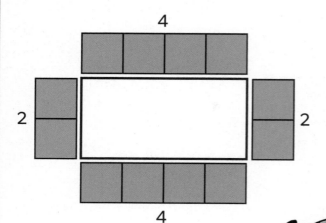

4

2

2

4

The lengths of all the sides are 4 + 2 + 4 + 2 squares long.

There are 12 squares in all.

You can use other objects to measure the lengths of the sides of a shape.

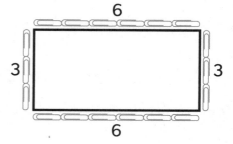

6

3

3

6

The lengths of all the sides are 6 + 3 + 6 + 3 paper clips long.

There are 18 paper clips in all.

Words to Know

length
how long an object is

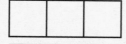

unit
an object used to measure length

DISCUSS Why does it take more paper clips than squares to measure the rectangle?

A You can use other objects to measure sides of a figure.

DO Measure the sides of the triangle.

1. Count the number of paper clips along each side.

2. Do not count paper clips that are longer than a side.

3. Write each side length.

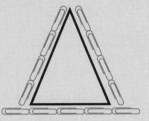

The bottom side is not 5 paper clips long.

The lengths of the sides are _____ + _____ + _____ paper clips.

B You can find the total lengths of the sides of a figure.

DO Find the total lengths of the sides of the pentagon.

1. Count the number of squares along each side.

2. Write the numbers to show each length.

3. Write how many squares in all.

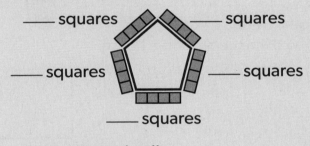

_____ squares   _____ squares

_____ squares   _____ squares

_____ squares

_____ squares in all

PRACTICE

Find the lengths of the sides of the figures.

 1

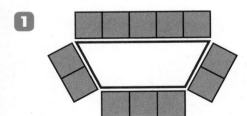

___3___ + _____ + _____ + _____ squares

_____ squares in all

2

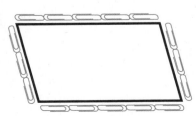

_____ + _____ + _____ + _____ paper clips

_____ paper clips in all

175

Measuring Perimeter

You can measure the lengths of the sides of a figure to find its **perimeter**.

The lengths of the rectangle are $5 + 2 + 5 + 2$ paper clips.

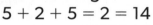

Add the lengths.
$5 + 2 + 5 = 2 = 14$

The figure is a rectangle, so I need to measure all 4 sides.

The perimeter of the rectangle is 14 paper clips.

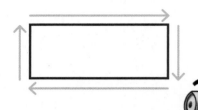

Words to Know

perimeter
the distance around a figure

DISCUSS Explain how you could find the perimeter of a triangle with sides that are each 8 paper clips long. What is the perimeter?

A You can use squares to find the perimeter of a figure.

DO Find the perimeter of the triangle.

1 Use squares to measure the length of each side.

2 Write the side lengths.

3 Add to find the perimeter.

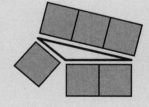

__3__ + _____ + _____ = _____

The perimeter of the triangle is _____ squares.

B You can measure and add the lengths of the sides to find the perimeter of a figure.

I don't count the bricks that are longer than a side.

 Find the perimeter of the rectangular garden.

1 Use bricks to measure the length of each side.

2 Write the lengths of the sides.

3 Add to find the perimeter.

___**3**___ + _____ + _____ + _____ = _____

The perimeter of the garden is _____ bricks.

 Rory used a pencil to measure the lengths of the sides of a frame. Rory said that the perimeter is 7 pencils long. What can you tell Rory about his work?

PRACTICE

Find the perimeter of each figure.

1

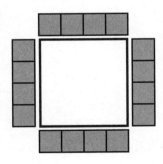

___**4**___ + _____ + _____ + _____ = _____

The perimeter is _____ squares.

2

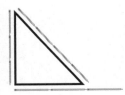

_____ + _____ + _____ = _____

The perimeter is _____ pencils.

Perimeter is the distance around a figure.

The figure is a pentagon, so it has 5 sides.

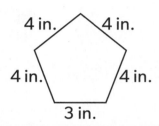

4 in.   4 in.

4 in.   4 in.

3 in.

Add the lengths of the sides.

4 in. + 4 in. + 4 in. + 4 in. + 3 in. = 19 in.

Four sides are 4 inches long. One side is 3 inches long.

The perimeter of the pentagon is 19 inches.

DISCUSS A circle does not have sides. Explain how you might find the perimeter of a circle.

LESSON LINK

PLUG IN   **POWER UP**   **GO!**

You can use different units to measure the lengths of the sides of a figure.

The side lengths of the rectangle are 4, 2, 4, and 2 paper clips.

I can count the total lengths of the sides to find the perimeter of a figure.

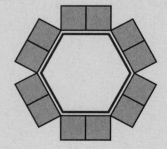

2 + 2 + 2 + 2 + 2 + 2 = 12

The perimeter of the figure is 12 squares.

I get it! I can add the lengths of the sides of a figure to find the perimeter!

WORK TOGETHER

You can multiply to find the perimeter of a figure if all its sides are the same length.

- The figure is a square. So all 4 sides are 3 centimeters long.
- Multiply 4 by 3 centimeters.
- The perimeter of the square is 12 centimeters.

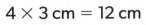

I get it! I can multiply the length of one side by the number of sides.

4×3 cm $= 12$ cm

A You can use multiplication to find the perimeter of some figures.

DO Find the perimeter of the pentagon.

1 The figure is a pentagon. Count the number of sides.

2 Check that the sides are the same length.

3 Use multiplication to find the perimeter.

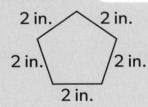

All ___**5**___ sides are _____ inches long.

_____ × _____ in. = _____ inch.

The perimeter of the pentagon is _____ inches.

B Use multiplication to find the perimeter.

DO Find the perimeter of a triangle with sides that are each 6 centimeters long.

1 Write the number of sides in a triangle.

2 Write the length of each side.

3 Use multiplication to find the perimeter.

All ___**3**___ sides are _____ centimeters long.

_____ × _____ cm = _____ cm

The perimeter is _____ centimeters.

DISCUSS How can you check your multiplication when finding perimeter for figures with all sides the same length?

PRACTICE

Use addition to find the perimeter.

1

6 in.

4 in. 4 in.

6 in.

6____ in. + _____ in. + _____ in. + _____ in. = _____ in.

The perimeter of the figure is _____ inches.

HINT
Add all the side lengths to find perimeter.

2 5 cm 5 cm

8 cm

_____ + _____ + _____ = _____

The perimeter of the triangle is _____ centimeters.

3

3 m

2 m 2 m

3 m

_____ + _____ + _____ + _____ = _____

The perimeter of the rectangle is _____ meters.

4 6 ft

6____ + _____ + _____ + _____ = _____

The perimeter of the square is _____ feet.

The sides of each shape are the same length. Use multiplication to find the perimeter.

5

5 in.

All _____ sides are _____ in. long.

_____ × _____ in. = _____ in.

The perimeter is _____ inches.

6

2 cm

All _____ sides are _____ cm long.

_____ × _____ cm = _____ cm

The perimeter is _____ centimeters.

Find the perimeter.

7 Amber wants to decorate her kite with ribbon trim around its edges. Her kite has four sides, and each side measures 10 inches. How many inches of ribbon does Amber need?

I can find the perimeter if I know the lengths of the sides!

_____ inches

DISCUSS

Missing Measures

Don measured some frames and wrote the side lengths and perimeter of each frame on a chart. He spilled his drink on the chart, so some of the numbers are missing. Help Don fix his chart by filling in the missing information.

Perimeter (inches)	Side Length (inches)	Side Length (inches)	Side Length (inches)	Side Length (inches)
24		7	5	5
	10	8	10	8
44	11		11	11
	4	6	4	6

What are two different ways you can find the perimeter using the side lengths?

PROBLEM SOLVING

FENCED IN

READ   A rectangular fence is 10 meters long and 5 meters wide. What is the perimeter of the fence?

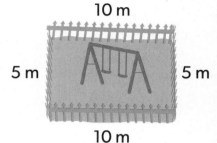

10 m

5 m   5 m

10 m

PLAN   • What is the problem asking you to find?

You need to find the _____ of the fence.

• What do you need to know to solve the problem?

How many meters long is the length of the fence?_____

How many meters long is the width of the fence?_____

• What should you do to find the perimeter of the fence?

You should add the lengths of all 4 sides.

SOLVE   Add the lengths of the sides to find the perimeter.

_____ + _____ + _____ + _____ = _____

CHECK   Make a diagram of the fence.

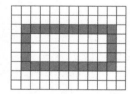

Count the shaded squares to find the perimeter.

The perimeter of the fence is _____ meters.

PRACTICE

Use the problem-solving steps to help you.

1 Amber drew the figure below in her notebook.

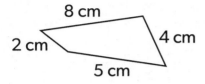

What is the perimeter of the figure?

CHECKLIST
☐ READ
☐ PLAN
☐ SOLVE
☐ CHECK

---

2 Caleb needs to find the perimeter of this triangle.

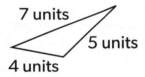

What is the perimeter of the triangle?

CHECKLIST
☐ READ
☐ PLAN
☐ SOLVE
☐ CHECK

---

3 Mr. Po plans to put a fence around his dog's play area. The sides are equal in length.

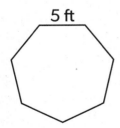

What is the perimeter of the play area?

CHECKLIST
☐ READ
☐ PLAN
☐ SOLVE
☐ CHECK

Area of Rectangles

PLUG IN Counting Squares

A **rectangle** can be divided into equal squares in **rows** and **columns**.

Count the squares.

1	2	3
4	5	6

The rectangle has 2 rows and 3 columns.

Rows are left to right. Columns are top to bottom.

There is a total of 6 squares.

Words to Know

rectangle a closed figure with 4 sides and 4 square corners

row left-to-right group

column top-to-bottom group

DISCUSS What addition sentence can you write to show the total number of squares in the rectangle above?

A You can count the number of squares in each row.

DO Count the squares in a rectangle with 2 rows and 4 columns.

❶ Count and write the number of squares in the top row.

❷ Count and write the number of squares in the next row.

❸ Add to find the total number of squares.

____4____ + _____ = _____ squares in all

Columns go top to bottom.

B You can count the number of squares in each column.

DO Count the squares in a rectangle with 3 columns and 5 rows.

1 Count and write the number of squares in the first column.

2 Count and write the number of squares in the 2nd and 3rd columns.

3 Add to find the total number of squares.

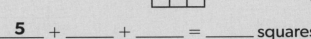

__5__ + _____ + _____ = _____ squares

PRACTICE

Write the number of squares in each row. Then write the number of squares in each column. Add to find each total.

1

__4__ + _____ + _____ = _____ squares

__3__ + _____ + _____ + _____ = _____ squares

2

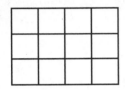

_____ + _____ + _____ + _____ + _____ = _____ squares

_____ + _____ = _____ squares

3

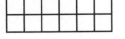

_____ + _____ = _____ squares

_____ + _____ + _____ + _____ + _____ + _____ = _____ squares

Understanding How to Measure Area

Area is the amount of space a shape covers. Area can be measured with **square units**.

1

1 ☐
1 square unit

The rectangle is divided into equal squares, or square units.

Count the square units to find the area.

1	2	3	4
5	6	7	8
9	10	11	12

There are 12 squares in the rectangle.

Each square is 1 square unit.

Area = 12 square units

The rectangle has 12 squares, so it has an area of 12 square units.

Words to Know

area
the amount of space a shape covers

Area = 10 square units

square unit
a square with side lengths of 1 unit

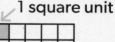
1 square unit

DISCUSS Is there a way to count squares more quickly? Explain your answer.

A You can find the area of a rectangle by counting rows of squares.

DO Find the area of the figure.

❶ Count each row of squares. Write the numbers.

❷ Add the number of squares in each row.

❸ Write the area in number of square units.

5

___ ___

___

___5___ + _____ + _____ = _____

Area = _____ square units

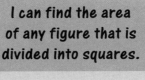

B You can find the area of other figures by counting squares.

 Find the area of the figure.

1 Count the squares.

2 Label the squares as you count.

3 Write the area in square units.

Area = _____ square units

 Sadie found the area of this rectangle by counting columns of squares. What can you tell Sadie about her work?

$3 + 3 + 3 = 9$ Area = 9 square units

PRACTICE

Find the area of each rectangle.

1
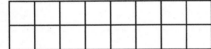

Area = _____ square units

2
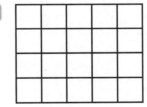

Area = _____ square units

Find the area of each figure.

3
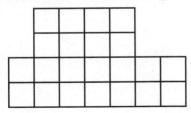

Area = _____ square units

4
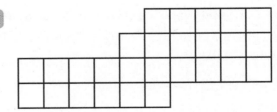

Area = _____ square units

A rectangle has **length** and **width**.

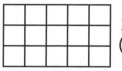

3 units
(width)

5 units
(length)

This rectangle has a length of 5 units and a width of 3 units.

Multiply the length and width to find the **area** of a rectangle.

Area = length × width = 5 × 3
Area = 15 square units

The area of the rectangle is 15 square units.

Words to Know

length
the measurement of the longer side of a rectangle

length

width
the measurement of the shorter side of a rectangle

width

area
the amount of space a shape covers

Area = 10 square units

DISCUSS Would the area be the same if you multiplied the width times the length? Explain.

LESSON LINK

PLUG IN	POWER UP	GO!

Count squares by rows or by columns to find the total number of squares.

Area is measured in square units.

1 square unit

Area = 2 units × 7 units
Area = 14 square units

I get it! Multiplication is another way to find the area of a rectangle.

WORK TOGETHER

Use Square Units to measure the area.

- This rectangle is 6 units long and 4 units wide.
- Multiply 6 × 4 to find the area.
- The area is 24 square units.

I can use multiplication to find the area.

4 units

6 units

Area = length × width = 6 × 4

Area = 24 square units

You can use squares and multiplication to find the area of a rectangle.

Square Units can be found on p. 233.

A Find the area of a rectangle that is 9 units long by 2 units wide.

DO

1. Show 9 units for the length.
2. Show 2 units for the width.
3. Multiply the length and the width.
4. Find the area.

Area = length × width

Area = _____ × _____ = _____ square units

B Find the area of a rectangle that is 7 units long by 3 units wide.

DO

1. Show 7 units for the length.
2. Show 3 units for the width.
3. Multiply the length and the width.
4. Find the area.

Area = length × width

Area = _____ × _____ = _____ square units

DISCUSS

Darius knows the area of a rectangle is 30 square units. The width of the rectangle is 5 units. How can Darius find the length of the rectangle?

What is the length of the rectangle?

PRACTICE

Use multiplication to find the area of each rectangle.

1

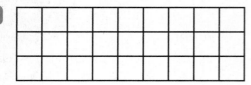

Area = ___9___ × _____ = _____ square units

2

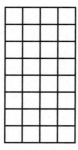

Area = _____ × _____ = _____ square units

3

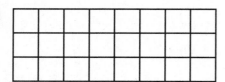

Area = _____ × _____ = _____ square units

4

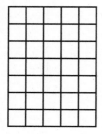

Area = _____ × _____ = _____ square units

5

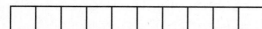

Area = ___10___ × _____ = _____ square units

Use the area and the width to find the length of each rectangle.

6 Area = 40 square units

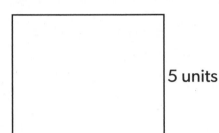

5 units

Length = _____ units

7 Area = 24 square units

4 units

Length = _____ units

I can use squares to show the area of the rectangle.

Solve.

8 Heidi drew a rectangle that measured 9 units long and
4 units wide. What is the area of Heidi's rectangle?   _____ square units

9 Luke knows the area of a rectangle is 50 square units.
The length of the rectangle is 10 units.
What is the width of the rectangle?   _____ units

DISCUSS

Model with Mathematics

Maria used 24 squares to make a rectangle 6 units long and 4 units wide.

She wants to know if there is another way to make a rectangle using the same number of squares.

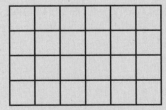

HINT
If you change
the order of
the factors in a
multiplication
equation, is
the product the
same?

How many different rectangles can Maria make? What are the length
and width of each?

PROBLEM SOLVING

SAND PLAY

READ | Hunter bought a rectangular sandbox measuring 6 feet long by 3 feet wide to put in his yard. How much of Hunter's yard will be covered by the sandbox?

PLAN | • What is the problem asking you to find?

You need to find the _____ of the sandbox in square _____ .

• What do you need to know to solve the problem?

What is the length? _____ feet

What is the width? _____ feet

• How can you find the area?

You can make a model using squares, or multiply the length times the width.

SOLVE | Make a model using squares.

Area = length × width

Area = 6 × _____ = _____ square feet

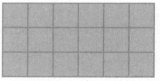

CHECK | Use repeated addition.

Write the number of squares in each row, and add.

_____ + _____ + _____ = _____

_____ total squares

Hunter's sandbox covers _____ square _____ of his yard.

PRACTICE

Use the problem-solving steps to help you.

1 Aisha has a rubber stamp of a butterfly. The stamp measures 7 centimeters long and 6 centimeters wide. What is the area of Aisha's stamp?

CHECKLIST
- [ ] READ
- [ ] PLAN
- [ ] SOLVE
- [ ] CHECK

2 Carlos painted one wall of his garden shed. The wall is 3 meters long and 2 meters high. What is the area of the wall Carlos painted?

CHECKLIST
- [ ] READ
- [ ] PLAN
- [ ] SOLVE
- [ ] CHECK

3 Mrs. Thompson bought a rug for her living room. The length of the rug is 10 feet. The width of the rug is 8 feet. How many square feet is Mrs. Thompson's rug?

CHECKLIST
- [ ] READ
- [ ] PLAN
- [ ] SOLVE
- [ ] CHECK

20 Classifying Shapes

PLUG IN Understanding Polygons

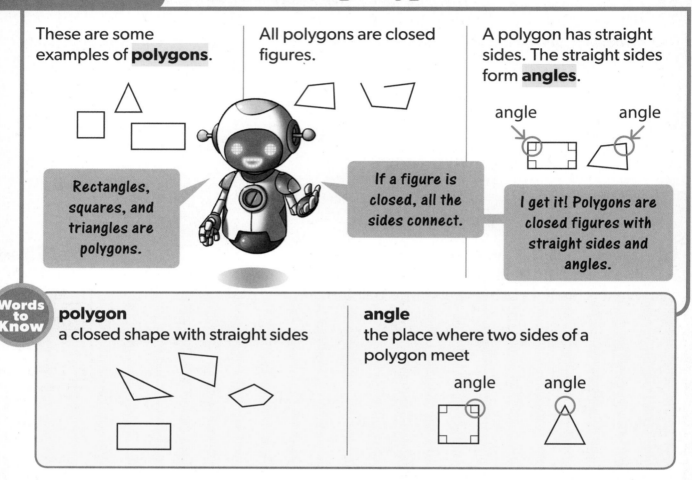

These are some examples of **polygons**.

All polygons are closed figures.

A polygon has straight sides. The straight sides form **angles**.

angle   angle

Rectangles, squares, and triangles are polygons.

If a figure is closed, all the sides connect.

I get it! Polygons are closed figures with straight sides and angles.

Words to Know

polygon
a closed shape with straight sides

angle
the place where two sides of a polygon meet

angle   angle

DISCUSS Is a circle a polygon? Why or why not?

A You can find polygons in a group of shapes.

DO Mark Xs on the shapes that are open. Circle the polygons.

❶ Put an X on the shapes that are open.

❷ Circle the closed shapes with only straight sides.

❸ Count the polygons.

❹ Write the number.

_____ polygons

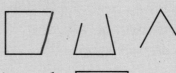
All sides of a polygon are straight.

B You can make open shapes into polygons.

DO Draw a straight line to make each shape a polygon.

1 Think about the sides of a polygon.

2 Draw a straight line to close each open shape.

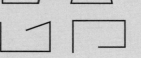

PRACTICE

Circle the polygons. Write the number of polygons.

1

_____**2**_____ polygons

2

_____ polygons

3

_____ polygons

4

_____ polygons

Draw a straight line to make the shape a polygon.

5

6

Identifying Shapes

Polygons are shapes that can be described by the number of sides. **Triangles**, **quadrilaterals**, and **pentagons** are polygons.

Polygons can also be described by their number of angles. A **hexagon** has 6 sides and 6 angles. *Hexa-* means "six."

angle

2

1   3

6   4

5

Triangles have 3 sides, quadrilaterals have 4 sides, and pentagons have 5 sides.

A polygon has the same number of sides as angles.

Words to Know

triangle a polygon with 3 sides and 3 angles	**quadrilateral** a polygon with 4 sides and 4 angles	**pentagon** a polygon with 5 sides and 5 angles	**hexagon** a polygon with 6 sides and 6 angles

DISCUSS If a polygon has 8 sides, how many angles will it have? How do you know?

A You can look at the sides and angles to identify polygons.

DO Write the number of sides and angles. Name each polygon.

1 Count the number of sides. Write the number.

2 Count the number of angles. Write the number.

3 Name the polygon.

__4__ sides   _____ sides   _____ sides

__4__ angles   _____ angles   _____ angles

_____   _____   _____

The prefix, penta-, means five.

B You can draw polygons if you know the number of sides and angles.

 Draw a polygon with 5 sides and 5 angles.

1 The first two sides are drawn to form one angle.

2 Use a ruler. Draw 3 more sides. Form a new angle each time.

3 Close the polygon when you draw the fifth side.

DISCUSS Michael says that this is a quadrilateral.
Jordan says it is a triangle.
Who is correct? Explain.

PRACTICE

Write the number of sides and angles. Name each polygon.

1

___**6**___ sides

_____ angles

_____

2

_____ sides

_____ angles

_____

Draw a polygon with the number of sides and angles.

3 4 sides and 4 angles

4 6 sides and 6 angles

READY TO GO | Classifying Shapes

Quadrilaterals are polygons with 4 sides.

Squares and **rectangles** have square corners.

Squares and **rhombuses** have equal sides.

square corner

square corner

All of these figures are quadrilaterals.

All squares are rectangles, but not all rectangles are squares.

All squares are rhombuses, but not all rhombuses are squares.

Words to Know

square
a quadrilateral with 4 equal sides and 4 square corners

rectangle
a quadrilateral with 4 sides and 4 square corners

rhombus
a quadrilateral with 4 equal sides

DISCUSS Why aren't all rhombuses squares?

LESSON LINK

| PLUG IN | POWER UP | GO! |

A polygon is a closed shape with straight sides.

polygons

Polygons are named by the number of sides and angles.

quadrilateral

I get it! Some polygons can be named in more than one way.

WORK TOGETHER

Use a grid to draw a shape.

• This polygon has 4 sides.

• The opposite sides are equal.

• The polygon has square corners.

• Name the polygon in two ways.

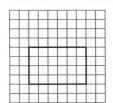

This polygon is a quadrilateral and a rectangle.

A Use the grid to draw a shape.

DO Draw a polygon with 4 equal sides and 4 square corners.

❶ Draw the length of the first side.

❷ Draw three more sides of equal length. Show the square corners.

❸ Name the polygon in 4 different ways.

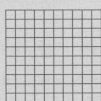

This polygon is a **quadrilateral**, a _____, a _____, and a _____.

B Use the grid to draw a shape.

DO Draw a polygon with 4 sides that are not equal.

❶ Draw the length of the first side.

❷ Draw three more sides of different lengths.

❸ Check that there are no square corners.

❹ Name the polygon.

This polygon is a _____.

DISCUSS Adam drew this shape on grid paper.

He says that his shape is a polygon, a quadrilateral, a rhombus, and a square. What can you tell Adam about his work?

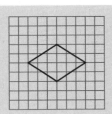

PRACTICE

Name each polygon.

1

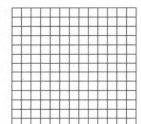

This polygon is a ___quadrilateral___ and

a _____.

2

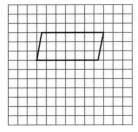

This polygon is a

_____.

Use the grid to draw each shape.

3 a polygon with 4 equal sides and 4 square corners

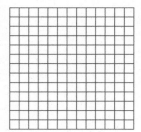

4 a polygon with 3 sides and 3 angles

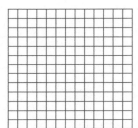

5 a polygon with 5 sides and 5 angles

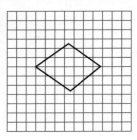

6 a polygon with 6 sides and 6 angles

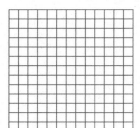

Use the grid to draw each shape. Then name the shape in 2 different ways.

7 a polygon with 4 sides, opposite sides are equal, and 4 square corners

8 a polygon with 4 equal sides and no square corners

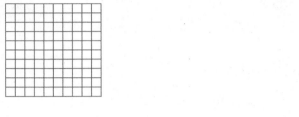

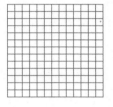

_____ and _____   _____ and _____

Solve.

9 Amit wants to draw a quadrilateral with 4 equal sides and 4 angles that are not equal.

What shape will he draw?   _____

10 Deana drew a quadrilateral that had 4 square corners, but its sides were not equal.

What polygon did Deana draw?   _____

DISCUSS   **Model the Math**

Hector drew a square on the grid. He wants to make a rectangle that is not a square by drawing another polygon and connecting it to the square.

Use the grid to finish drawing Hector's rectangle.

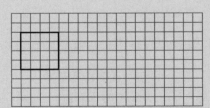

What polygon did you help Hector draw? Explain why the final shape is a rectangle.

PROBLEM SOLVING

POLYGON PUZZLES

READ — Jan's polygon has fewer than 5 sides and all sides are equal in length. It also has 4 square corners. What could Jan's polygon be?

PLAN —
- What is the problem asking you to find?

   You need to find what _____ could be Jan's.

- What do you need to know to solve the problem?

   How many sides does her polygon have? _____

   Are the sides equal in length? _____

   How many square corners? _____

- How can you find which polygon is Jan's?

   You can use grid paper and draw polygons.

SOLVE — Use grid paper to draw polygons.

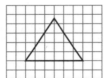   

This polygon has _____ sides.
The sides are equal in length.
It doesn't have square corners.

It is a _____.
This is not Jan's polygon.

This polygon has _____ sides.
The sides are equal in length.
It has square corners.

It is a _____.
This could be Jan's polygon.

CHECK — Think about other names for the polygon you chose.

Is a square a
quadrilateral?

_____

Is a square a
rhombus?

_____

Is a square a
rectangle?

_____

Jan's polygon could be a _____, a _____,

a _____, or a _____.

PRACTICE

Use the problem-solving steps to help you.

1 Laurel drew a polygon with 4 square corners.

The sides are not the same length.

What could be the name of Laurel's polygon?

2 Carrie drew a polygon with 4 angles.

None of the angles are square corners.

The sides are not the same length.

What could be the name of Carrie's polygon?

3 Greg drew a polygon with sides that are the same length.

None of the angles are square corners.

The polygon has fewer than 6 sides.

He did not draw a quadrilateral.

What could be the name of Greg's polygon?

Glossary

addition (add) to combine two or more values to find the sum or the total (Lesson 5)

$$3 + 5 = 8$$

A.M. between midnight and noon (Lesson 13)

angle where two sides of a polygon meet (Lesson 20)

area the amount of space that covers a figure (Lesson 19)

Area = 10 square units

array an arrangement with equal rows and columns (Lesson 7)

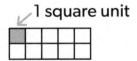

bar graph a graph that uses bars of different lengths to represent data (Lesson 16)

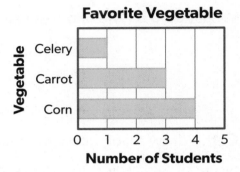

capacity the amount of liquid a container can hold (Lesson 14)

liquid volume: 2 liters

column a vertical arrangement of items (Lessons 7, 19)

compare to describe whether numbers are equal to, less than, or greater than each other (Lesson 4)

$$\frac{1}{3} < \frac{2}{3}$$

data numerical information
(Lessons 15, 16, 17)

3 students have cats
6 students have dogs
2 students have fish

denominator the bottom number in a fraction; tells the number of equal parts (Lessons 1, 3, 17)

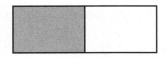

$$\frac{1}{2} \leftarrow \text{denominator}$$

distributive property of multiplication states that multiplying the sum of two numbers by a factor is the same as multiplying each addend by that factor, then adding the products (Lesson 8)

$$
\begin{aligned}
5 \times 2 &= 5 \times (1 + 1) \\
&= (5 \times 1) + (5 \times 1) \\
&= 5 + 5 \\
&= 10
\end{aligned}
$$

dividend the number that is being divided in a division sentence (Lesson 9)

$$6 \div 3 = 2$$
↑
dividend

division (divide) an operation on two numbers that tells how many equal groups or how many in each group (Lessons 10, 12)

divisor the number that is divided by in a division sentence (Lesson 9)

$$6 \div \mathbf{3} = 2$$
↑
divisor

elapsed time the amount of time that passes from the start of an activity to the end of that activity (Lesson 13)

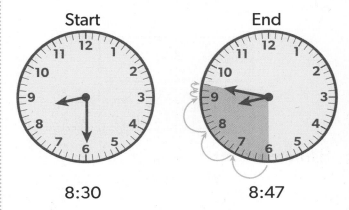

Start   End

8:30   8:47

elapsed time: 17 minutes

equal parts two or more numbers that have the same amount or value; the parts are the same size (Lesson 1)

equal to having the same amount or value (Lesson 4)

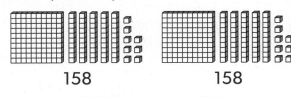

158   158

158 is equal to 158
158 = 158

equation a number sentence with an equal sign (Lessons 8, 11)

$$5 + 3 = 8$$
$$12 - 7 = 5$$
$$6 \times 2 = 12$$
$$24 \div 4 = 6$$

equivalent fractions fractions that have different numerators and denominators but name the same amount (Lesson 3)

$\frac{1}{2}$		$\frac{1}{2}$	
$\frac{1}{4}$	$\frac{1}{4}$	$\frac{1}{4}$	$\frac{1}{4}$

estimate to make a rough or approximate calculation, often based on rounding (Lesson 11)

$$\begin{array}{r} 71 \\ -33 \end{array} \rightarrow \begin{array}{r} 70 \\ -30 \\ \hline 40 \end{array}$$

even number a number with 0, 2, 4, 6, or 8 in the ones place (Lesson 12)

1<u>0</u>, 2<u>4</u>, 3<u>2</u>, 4<u>8</u>

fact family a group of related addition and subtraction facts or a group of related multiplication and division facts; related facts use the same numbers (Lesson 11)

$8 + 4 = 12$
$4 + 8 = 12$
$12 - 4 = 8$
$12 - 8 = 4$

$4 \times 8 = 32$
$8 \times 4 = 32$
$32 \div 4 = 8$
$32 \div 8 = 4$

factors numbers being multiplied in a multiplication problem (Lessons 7, 10)

$$3 \times 4 = 12$$
$$\underbrace{}_{\text{factors}}$$

fraction a number that names part of a whole (Lessons 3, 17)

$\frac{1}{2}$	$\frac{1}{2}$

The shaded part is $\frac{1}{2}$ of the whole.

fraction strip a model of a whole divided into unit fractions that have the same denominator (Lesson 4)

$\frac{1}{5}$	$\frac{1}{5}$	$\frac{1}{5}$	$\frac{1}{5}$	$\frac{1}{5}$

gram (g) a metric unit of mass; 1,000 grams = 1 kilogram (Lesson 14)

1 gram

greater than more than; shows relationships between numbers (Lesson 4)

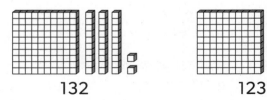

132   123

132 is greater than 123
132 > 123

hexagon a polygon with 6 sides and 6 angles (Lesson 20)

hour hand the short hand on a clock; tells the hour (Lesson 13)

inverse operation an operation that undoes another operation; addition and subtraction are inverse operations; multiplication and division are inverse operations (Lesson 11)

$$8 + 4 = 12 \qquad 3 \times 4 = 12$$
$$12 - 4 = 8 \qquad 12 \div 4 = 3$$

key tells how many each symbol represents (Lesson 15)

Key: Each ✏ = 1 student

kilogram (kg) a metric unit of mass; 1 kilogram = 1,000 grams (Lesson 14)

1 kilogram

length the measure of how long, how wide, or how tall an object is (Lessons 18, 19)

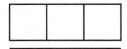

less than not as many as; shows relationships between numbers (Lesson 4)

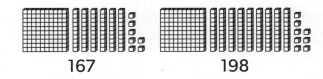

167   198

167 is less than 198
$$167 < 198$$

line plot a display that uses Xs above a number line to represent data (Lesson 17)

String

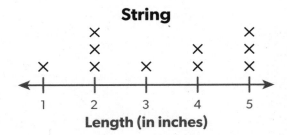

Length (in inches)

liquid volume the amount of liquid a container can hold (Lesson 14)

liquid volume: 2 liters

liter (L) a metric unit of capacity; 1 liter = 1,000 milliliters (Lesson 14)

1 liter

mass the amount of matter in an object (Lesson 14)

milliliters (mL) a metric unit of capacity; 1,000 milliliters = 1 liter (Lesson 14)

1 milliliter

minute hand the long hand on a clock; tells the minute (Lesson 13)

multiplication (multiply) an operation that joins equal groups (Lessons 7, 12)

$$3 \times 4 = 12$$

number line line marked with numbers, used to show operations (Lessons 1, 7)

numerator the top number in a fraction (Lessons 1, 3, 17)

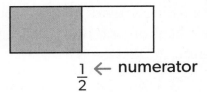

$\frac{1}{2}$ ← numerator

odd number a number with 1, 3, 5, 7, or 9 in the ones place (Lesson 12)

1<u>3</u>, 2<u>1</u>, 3<u>7</u>, 4<u>5</u>, 4<u>9</u>

one-half one of two equal parts (Lesson 2)

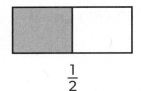

$\frac{1}{2}$

one-third one of three equal parts (Lesson 2)

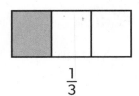

$\frac{1}{3}$

pattern repeated design or recurring sequence (Lesson 12)

10, 12, 14, 16, 18, 20
(increase by 2 each time)

pentagon a polygon with 5 sides and 5 angles (Lesson 20)

perimeter the distance around a figure (Lesson 18)

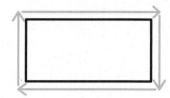

picture graph a graph that uses symbols to represent data (Lessons 15, 16)

Favorite Color

Blue	✏️✏️
Green	✏️✏️✏️✏️
Red	✏️✏️✏️
Yellow	✏️

Key: Each ✏️ = 1 student

place value the value of a digit depending upon its place in a number (Lessons 6, 11)

Hundreds	Tens	Ones
7	4	3

place-value chart a chart that shows the value of a digit based on where it is in the number (Lessons 5, 6)

Tens	Ones
5	6

P.M. between noon and midnight (Lesson 13)

polygon a closed shape with three or more straight sides (Lesson 20)

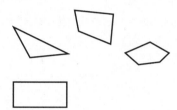

product the answer in a multiplication problem (Lessons 7, 10, 12)

$$3 \times 4 = \textbf{12}$$
↑
product

quadrilateral a polygon with 4 sides and 4 angles (Lesson 20)

quotient the answer in a division problem (Lessons 9, 10, 12)

$$6 \div 3 = \textbf{2}$$
↑
quotient

rectangle a quadrilateral with four sides and four angles that are square corners (Lessons 19, 20)

regroup to rename a number by exchanging amounts of equal value (Lessons 5, 6)

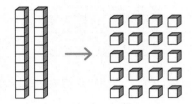

repeated addition adding the same number more than once (Lesson 8)

rhombus a quadrilateral with two pairs of parallel sides and four equal sides (Lesson 20)

round a way to estimate numbers (Lesson 11)

462

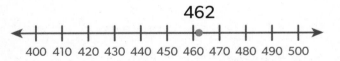

400 410 420 430 440 450 460 470 480 490 500

462 is closer to 460 than to 470.
462 is closer to 500 than to 400.

row a horizontal arrangement of items (Lessons 7, 19)

scale (in a bar graph) gives the value of each bar in the graph (Lesson 16)

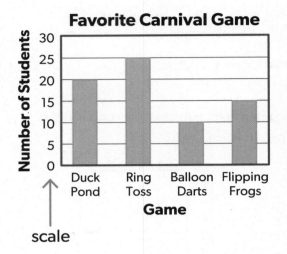

Favorite Carnival Game

scale

skip count to count forward or backward in multiples of intervals of a given number (Lesson 7)

5, 10, 15, 20, 25

skip count backward to count backward by the same number (Lesson 9)

square a quadrilateral with two pairs of parallel sides, four equal sides, and four right angles (Lesson 20)

square unit a square that has the side length of one unit (Lesson 19)

1 square unit

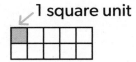

subtraction (subtract) an operation that takes a value away from another value to find the difference (Lesson 6)

$$8 - 3 = 5$$

triangle a polygon with 3 sides and 3 angles (Lesson 20)

unit an object used to measure length (Lesson 18)

unit fraction a fraction that names one equal part of a whole (Lesson 1)

width distance across from side to side (Lesson 19)

Math Tool: Place-Value Models

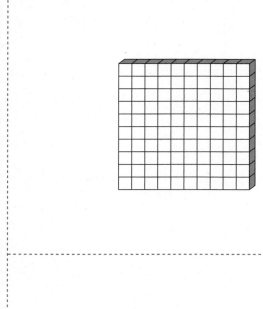

  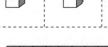

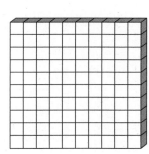

 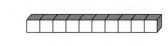 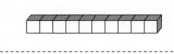

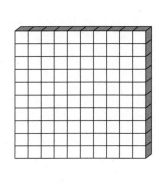

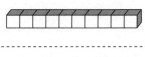 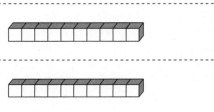 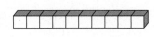

Math Tool: Place-Value Models

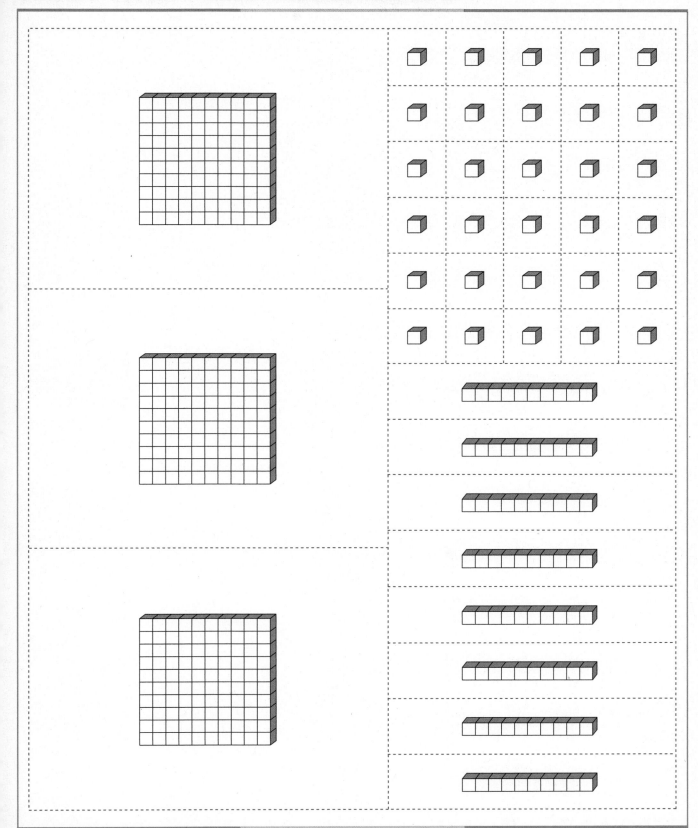

Name _____   Date _____

Math Tool: Grouping Mat

Name _____ Date _____

Math Tool: Counters

Math Tool: Grouping Mat

Name _____ Date _____

Math Tool: Counters

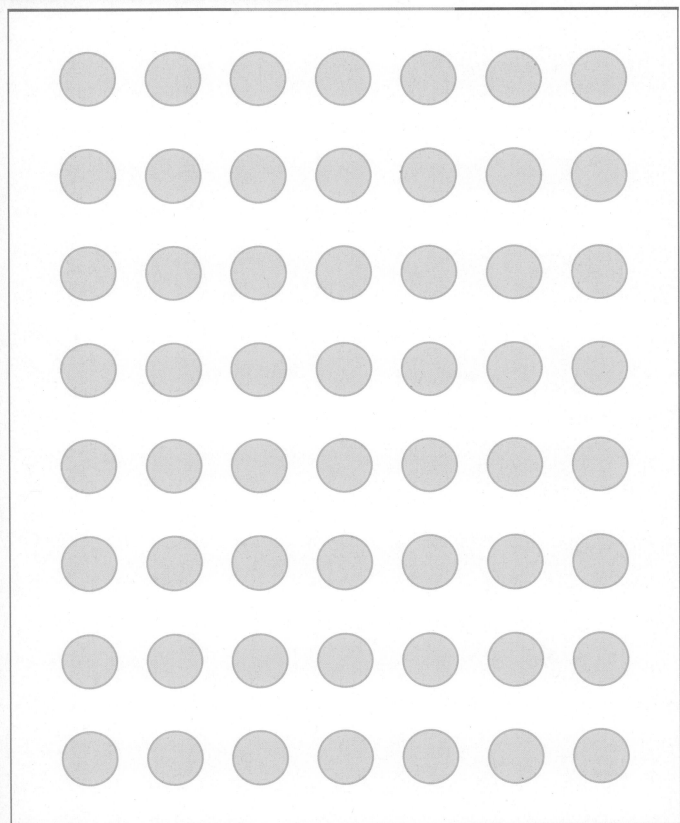

Math Tool: Grouping Mat

Math Tool: Counters

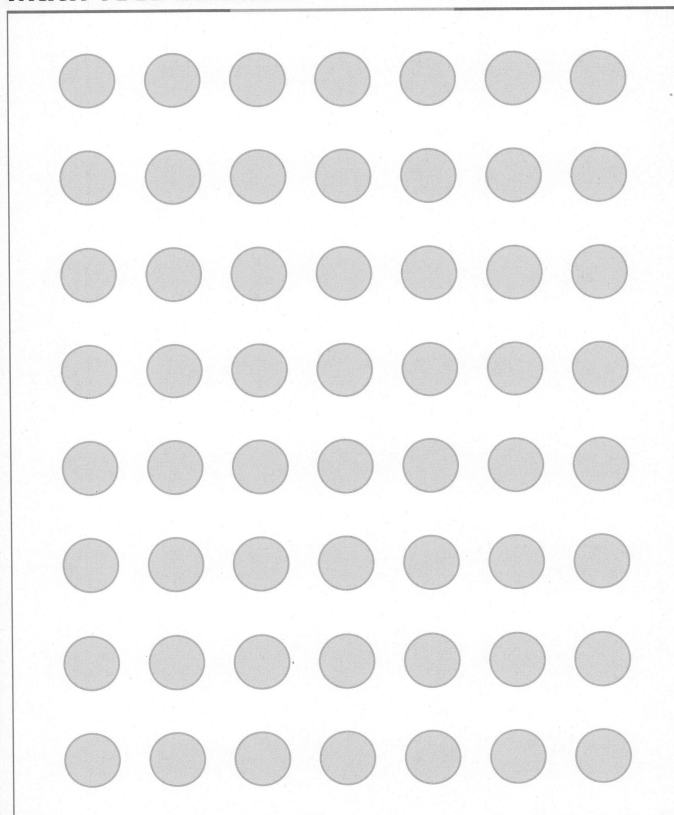

Math Tool: Multiplication Table

×	0	1	2	3	4	5	6	7	8	9	10
0	0	0	0	0	0	0	0	0	0	0	0
1	0	1	2	3	4	5	6	7	8	9	10
2	0	2	4	6	8	10	12	14	16	18	20
3	0	3	6	9	12	15	18	21	24	27	30
4	0	4	8	12	16	20	24	28	32	36	40
5	0	5	10	15	20	25	30	35	40	45	50
6	0	6	12	18	24	30	36	42	48	54	60
7	0	7	14	21	28	35	42	49	56	63	70
8	0	8	16	24	32	40	48	56	64	72	80
9	0	9	18	27	36	45	54	63	72	81	90
10	0	10	20	30	40	50	60	70	80	90	100

Math Tool: Blank Number Lines

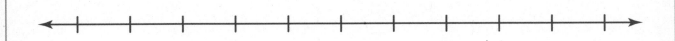

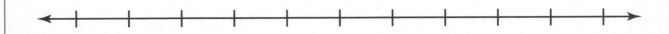

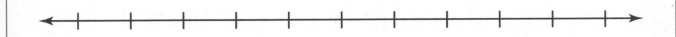

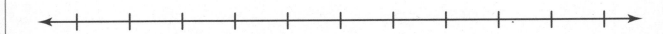

Name _____ Date _____

Math Tool: Square Units

Math Tool: Fraction Strips

1

$\dfrac{1}{2}$	$\dfrac{1}{2}$

$\dfrac{1}{3}$	$\dfrac{1}{3}$	$\dfrac{1}{3}$

$\dfrac{1}{4}$	$\dfrac{1}{4}$	$\dfrac{1}{4}$	$\dfrac{1}{4}$

$\dfrac{1}{6}$	$\dfrac{1}{6}$	$\dfrac{1}{6}$	$\dfrac{1}{6}$	$\dfrac{1}{6}$	$\dfrac{1}{6}$

$\dfrac{1}{8}$	$\dfrac{1}{8}$	$\dfrac{1}{8}$	$\dfrac{1}{8}$	$\dfrac{1}{8}$	$\dfrac{1}{8}$	$\dfrac{1}{8}$	$\dfrac{1}{8}$

Math Tool: Grid Paper

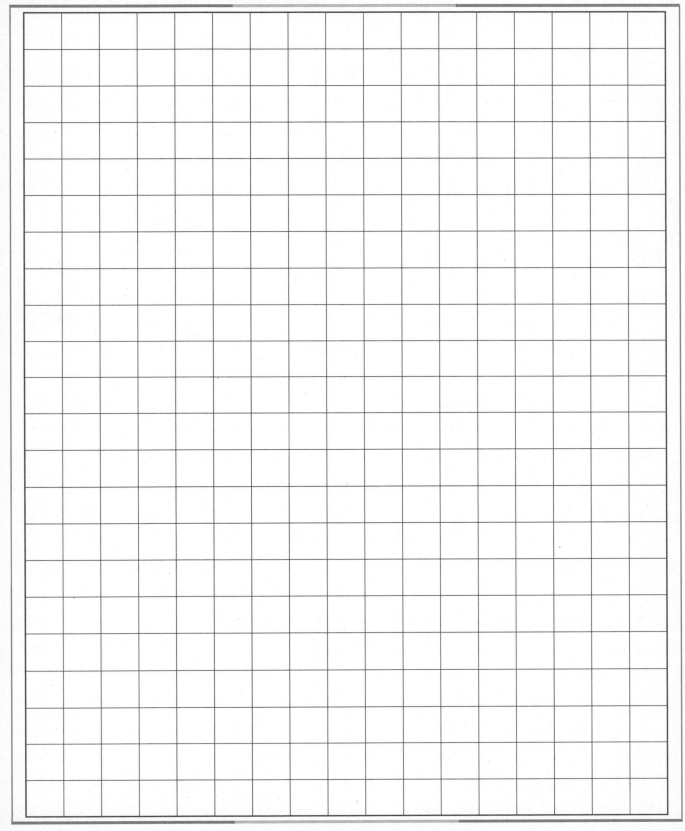

Math Tool: Place-Value Charts

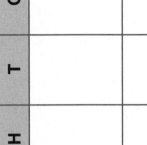

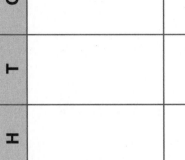

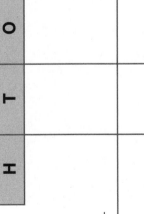

Math Tool: Addition Table

+	0	1	2	3	4	5	6	7	8	9	10
0	0	1	2	3	4	5	6	7	8	9	10
1	1	2	3	4	5	6	7	8	9	10	11
2	2	3	4	5	6	7	8	9	10	11	12
3	3	4	5	6	7	8	9	10	11	12	13
4	4	5	6	7	8	9	10	11	12	13	14
5	5	6	7	8	9	10	11	12	13	14	15
6	6	7	8	9	10	11	12	13	14	15	16
7	7	8	9	10	11	12	13	14	15	16	17
8	8	9	10	11	12	13	14	15	16	17	18
9	9	10	11	12	13	14	15	16	17	18	19
10	10	11	12	13	14	15	16	17	18	19	20

Name _____   Date _____

Math Tool: 10 x 10 grids

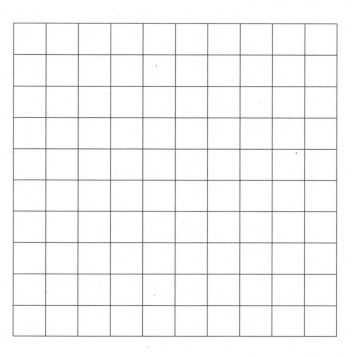

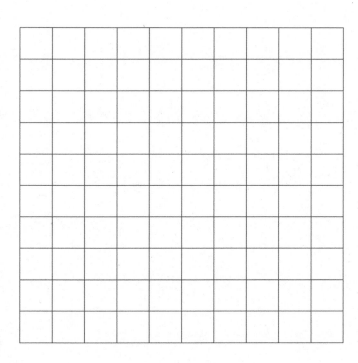

Math Tool: Blank Number Lines

0   1

0   1

0   1

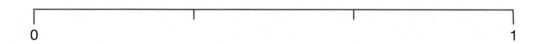

0   1

0   1

Math Tool: Place-Value Models

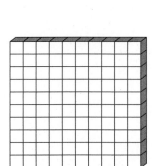

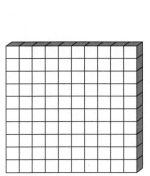

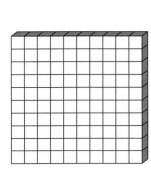

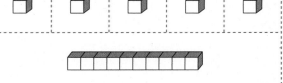

Name _____ Date _____

Math Tool: **Counters**

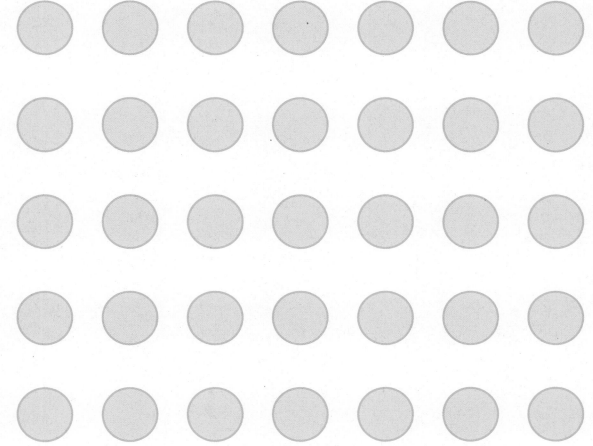

Math Tool: Grouping Mat

Math Tool: Multiplication Table

×	0	1	2	3	4	5	6	7	8	9	10
0	0	0	0	0	0	0	0	0	0	0	0
1	0	1	2	3	4	5	6	7	8	9	10
2	0	2	4	6	8	10	12	14	16	18	20
3	0	3	6	9	12	15	18	21	24	27	30
4	0	4	8	12	16	20	24	28	32	36	40
5	0	5	10	15	20	25	30	35	40	45	50
6	0	6	12	18	24	30	36	42	48	54	60
7	0	7	14	21	28	35	42	49	56	63	70
8	0	8	16	24	32	40	48	56	64	72	80
9	0	9	18	27	36	45	54	63	72	81	90
10	0	10	20	30	40	50	60	70	80	90	100

Math Tool: Square Units

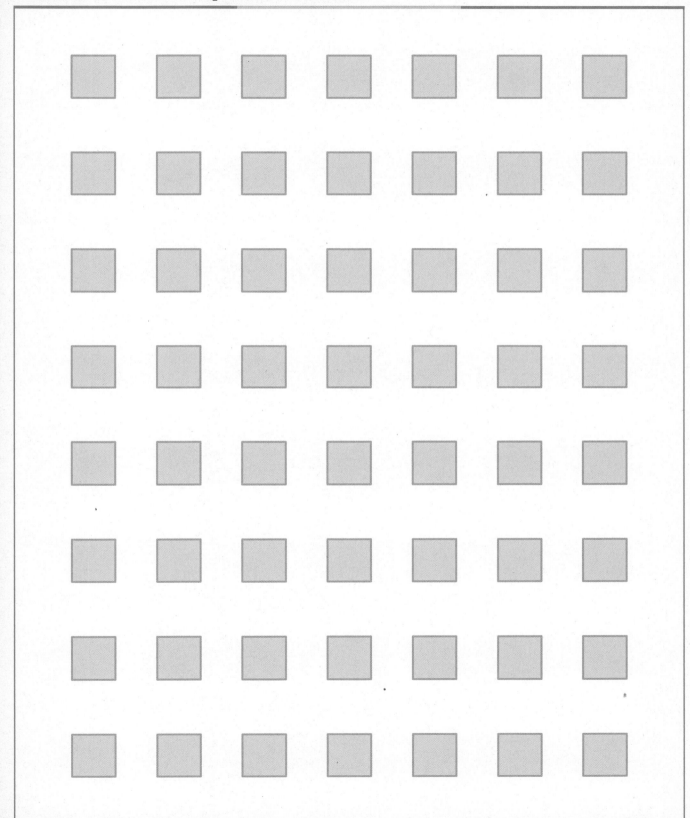

Common Core Support Coach

TARGET ▸ Foundational Mathematics

Developed Exclusively for the CCSS

Master the key concepts you need
to succeed in math!

FOCUS ON

> Whole Numbers and Fractio...
> Multiplication and Division
> Time, Capacity, and Mass
> Picture Graphs, Bar Graphs, and Line Plots
> Perimeter and Area
> Working with Shapes

www.triumphlearning.com

Phone: (800) 338-6519 • Fax: (866) 805-5723 • E-mail: customerservice@triumphlearning.com

ISBN-13: 978-1-61997-974-1

triumphlearning™

T198NA

Triumph Online™ • Coach™ • Buckle Down™ • Options™